90

W9-CHB-205

SOUTH PORTLAND PUBLIC LIBRARY

3 3940 00058 1551

NEW WORLDS
through the
MICROSCOPE

The antenna of a moth.

NEW WORLDS
through the
MICROSCOPE
by Robert Disraeli

Every grain of sand is an immensity,
Every leaf a world.
                    —LAVATER

WITHDRAWN

New York • The Viking Press

BRANCH   South Portland
          Public Library

Copyright © 1933, 1939, 1960 by Robert Disraeli
All rights reserved

First published under the title *Seeing the Unseen* in 1933
by The John Day Company, Inc.; revised edition 1939.
Reissued in 1960 with many new photographs and revised expanded text
by The Viking Press, Inc., 625 Madison Avenue, New York 22, N. Y.

Distributed in Canada by
The Macmillan Company of Canada Limited
Library of Congress catalog card number: 60-11913
Fourth printing June 1966

578   1. BIOLOGY
         2. MICROSCOPE AND MICROSCOPY

ACKNOWLEDGMENTS

Thanks are due to Mr. J. J. Host of American Optical Company
for his cooperation, and to my wife for her encouragement.

PRINTED IN THE U.S.A. BY MURRAY PRINTING COMPANY

Contents

Discovering New Worlds   9

How To Look   13

Tools   16

The Insect   23

The Eggs of Insects   26

The Offspring of Insects   28

How the Insect Eats   38

How the Insect Feels   45

How the Insect Sees   48

How the Insect Walks   52

How the Insect Flies   59

The Fly   67

The Ant   69

The Spider   71

The Sponge   75

The Protozoa   81

The Cell   85

The Algae   91

The Fungi   102

The Mosses   111

The Leaf   117

The Root   122

Pollen and Seeds   126

Starch   138

Hair, Feathers, and Scales   141

Blood   155

Dust   157

Cloth   159

Crystals   164

Paper   171

How to Continue   173

NEW WORLDS
through the
MICROSCOPE

Discovering New Worlds

Go down to the seashore—on some quiet beach where there are few people—and look about you. What do you see?

The sky, of course, and the sea; sand, pebbles, and rocks; perhaps a few clam shells on the sand. Not a sign of life, you think. Even if you look closely at a little slime from the rocks, a seaweed, a little wet sand, a small jar of water from the sea or from one of the pools left by the retreating tide, you may see nothing alive. But look at them in another way and you will be astonished. Under the microscope you will see sensitive, living creatures swimming or creeping in all of them. In the drops of water you have collected you will see hundreds, perhaps thousands, of the smallest known type of animal life. You will find other creatures clinging to the seaweed, and the slime from the rocks will be revealed as some of the simplest plants—beautiful plants, too. The seaweed itself is just as fascinating.

You discover that the beach which you thought deserted is alive with invisible wonders. Between high and low tide you find it swarming with hundreds of types of animals and plants struggling ceaselessly for existence.

Life is beginning and growing and dying all around you, all

9

the time, in the ocean and on the seashore, in the smallest brooks and largest rivers, in rain puddles and lakes, in woods and fields, and in the city as well as in the country. The first look through a microscope is as thrilling as a look into a new world. Your microscope can show you worlds as new and strange and exciting as any that a space rocket could find beyond the moon.

You need not look for rare and unusual specimens to examine under your microscope. Wonders are all around you. From a short walk through field or wood you can come home with enough things to keep you busy for many days, taking them apart and examining them. A bit of moss, a fern, a blade of grass with stem and root, wild flowers and simple weeds—these are easy to find. You can scarcely miss insects, and they are of constant interest. The green growth on rocks or the bark of trees, the pool of water left from yesterday's rain, the rotting log you open with your penknife carefully—all these are good objects for your microscope.

Now, after you have gathered and studied these objects for a while, go back to the seashore or go back to the country. How different everything looks! Life is everywhere! A tree is no longer a piece of wood but a community of cells that work harmoniously together for a common existence. Water is no longer clean or dirty, but a world full of thousands of forms of life. The soil is not just earth but is alive with hundreds of minute plants and animals.

You will become aware that this earth is a place of marvelous creations. There are no greater wonders in the distant stars than those revealed by your microscope. The world in a drop of water is as mysterious to us as the possible worlds of the farthest galaxies.

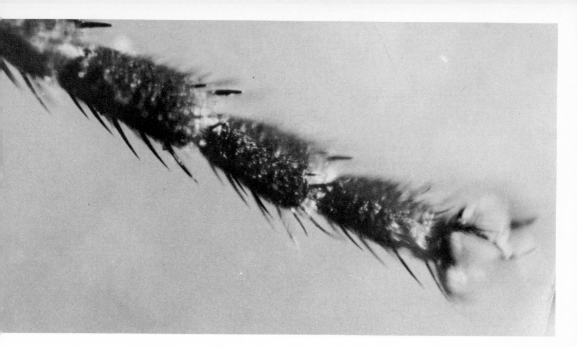

The leg of a fly seen through a microscope.

How To Look

The first look at the leg of a fly through a microscope is surprising. But after you have seen it several times you will lose interest unless you keep asking yourself questions, as a scientist does.

Why is the leg of a fly formed that way?

What are the hairs for?

How many sections has a fly's leg? Why should it have so many?

Why isn't it like the human leg?

How does the fly walk upside down, and why should he?

What kind of legs have other insects, and how are they like the fly's leg, and why?

Curiosity is the foundation of all science. Men have been

13

asking these questions a long time, and have given their lives to finding out the answers you are looking for now. The sciences have grown by simple questions: *What* is it? *How* does this work? *Why* does it work that way? There are many books to answer the questions and your librarian can help you. The science instructor in your school will be glad to answer your questions though you may not be in his class. He can guide you to the right books and advise you where to buy the materials for your needs. Never hesitate to ask questions. And if you don't understand, do not be afraid to admit it. Don't think you are the only one who cannot understand something the first time!

Girls, and even some boys, have told me that they couldn't possibly touch a bug. To them it was repulsive. The microscope will help you to get this idea out of your mind. There is nothing odious or revolting in nature. A creature may be strange to us but never loathsome. The feel of its body, the fact that it is built like nothing we ever saw before may indeed be queer or even startling. It may live in places we think ugly or even impossible for life—dark, wet, or decaying. But nothing in nature is disgusting. All life harmonizes with its own surroundings, and the more you study living things the more you will realize this and admire the beauty of the way in which everything fits together and makes one great whole.

You may say, "I live in a city, far from woods and water. I can't get these plants and insects." Oh, yes you can. You don't need to go to the woods or the seashore. Your neighborhood park, your own yard or an empty lot, even your mother's kitchen cupboard with its salt, sugar, spices, syrup, jellies, jams and other foods will give you many interesting specimens to examine through your microscope.

14

Tiny mushrooms grow among decaying leaves on the forest floor.

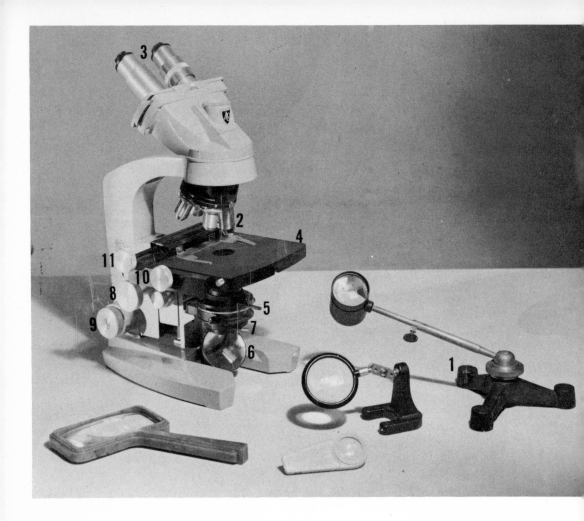

Tools

How will we begin? Start with simple tools, for only after you have mastered them can you be skillful in the use of more complicated ones.

The accompanying photograph shows the tools for seeing small objects. Magnifying glasses (1) are simple microscopes. They are necessary for studying and dissecting specimens. Those on adjustable stands leave your hands free to work. The others are good for quick and general examinations especially when collecting materials.

The large instrument is a compound microscope because it has two separate lenses. One lens is called the objective (2) and is close to the specimen. In this picture you see four lenses or objectives which have different magnifying powers. The lens close to the eye is the eyepiece (3) which magnifies the image formed by the objective. For example, if the objective magnifies 10 times and the eyepiece magnifies 5 times, the total magnification of the specimen is $10 \times 5 = 50$ times.

The picture shows a binocular microscope. It has two eyepieces. There are many fine microscopes with only one eyepiece which magnify equally as much and as well.

Below the objective lens is the stage (4), a platform for the glass slide on which the specimen is placed. Clamps hold the glass slide in place. Below the stage is the condenser (5) which gathers together the light from the adjustable mirror (6) and directs it upward through a hole in the stage to illuminate the transparent specimen.

The amount of light reaching the specimen is controlled by a diaphragm (7) that forms a round opening, the size of which can be varied.

To get a sharp image of the specimen, the stage may be moved toward or away from the objective lens by two knobs. The first (8) is the coarse-adjustment knob for a general focusing of the specimen. The second (9) is the fine-adjustment knob for seeing the specimen very clearly through the eyepiece. Two knobs also move the stage. The first (10) moves the stage toward the right or the left and the second (11) toward the viewer

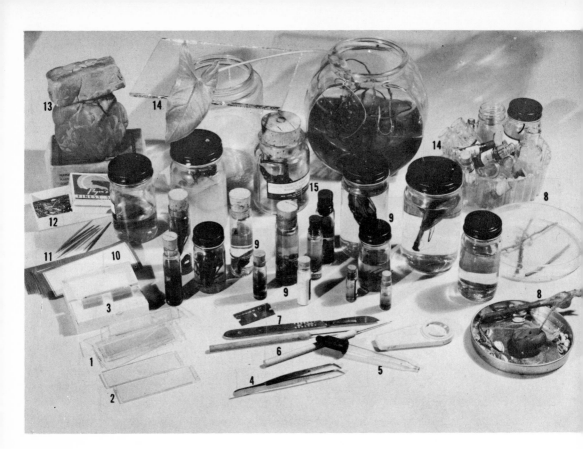

or away from him. These movements are useful for examining the entire specimen.

In some microscopes the stage cannot be moved, but the tube which holds the eyepiece and the objective moves up and down.

When a non-transparent specimen, such as the head of a fly, is placed on the stage, the light must come from above and from the front of the stage, since the light from the mirror below cannot penetrate opaque objects.

You will also need the following equipment: flat glass slides (1) on which to place solid objects for microscopic examination; glass slides with a cavity in the center (2) in which to place drops of liquid; cover glasses (3) to go over the specimens on the slides; forceps (4) to pick up material (a good eyebrow tweezer will do); an eye-dropper (5) for placing drops of liquid in the cavity slides; dissecting needles (6) for taking objects apart; a dissecting knife (scalpel) (7) and a one-edged razor blade to cut sections of materials; shallow metal, plastic, or glass dishes (8) for holding odds and ends; small and large vials and bottles (9), with lids or cork stoppers, in which to store liquids, insects, and other specimens. Some corks should have holes punched in them with a red-hot hairpin so that insects will not smother. Other useful things are: labels (10) to paste on jars to identify specimens; toothpicks (11), finely pointed, which can be used to move objects or to mount opaque objects on glass slides; pins (12) to hold objects in position on soft clean wood or a bed of clay for careful dissection; and gray or white modeling clay (13) for placing small opaque objects, such as an insect head, upon a glass slide or other support. Glass jars (14) for collecting samples of water in which there is plant and animal life are also useful for growing plants which thus can be studied continually. When taking water samples, fill the jar only halfway and keep it uncovered as long as possible. Take the cover off immediately when reaching home or the specimens may die. Small boxes will have many uses.

In most instances an insect must be killed before its parts can be studied under the microscope. A non-poisonous killing bottle (15) is the best method. After inserting the insect, put the bottle in a dark place. After an hour examine the insect in the bottle but do not remove it unless it is dead. Do not use this bottle for any other purpose. Always keep the cover on tightly even when it is not in use. And always wash your hands after you have used this bottle.

Cleanliness is absolutely essential when you are using the microscope. Not only your hands, but all objects—microscope, slides, glasses—should always be clean. A booklet of lens paper costs little and will keep your lenses clean without scratching the glass. When the instrument is not in use it should be kept in its case, or covered carefully to protect it from dust.

Always do your work facing daylight or an electric light.

Place your microscope on a firm and steady table. Allow no clothing, record players, or other possessions to lie on the table at the same time. Give yourself plenty of room when you are doing microscopy.

Your reward will be many hours of pleasure with your microscope.

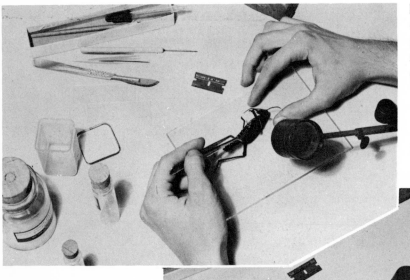

Before investigating any part of a specimen under the microscope, study it in its entirety.

After deciding which part of the specimen is to be studied, dissect it very carefully. One way of holding the specimen down is to place a roll of clay around it. Make clean, firm cuts. Work under the magnifying glass.

The part selected for microscope examination should be mounted neatly and firmly. When the part is thick and opaque, it can be placed on the clay-tipped end of a toothpick which, in turn, is inserted in a small lump of clay on the slide. The toothpick can then be turned to any position so that the specimen may be examined from all sides.

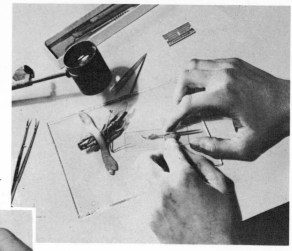

A small drop of liquid is enough for a cavity cell. Do not fill the cavity to the top or the liquid will spill over when you move the slide.

A square or round piece of very thin cover glass will help to keep the specimen on the slide. Build a thin ribbon-like wall of clay around a solid, thick specimen.

Slight pressure on the cover glass will fasten it firmly to the clay without damaging your specimen.

A cover glass always should be placed above a liquid in a cavity slide.

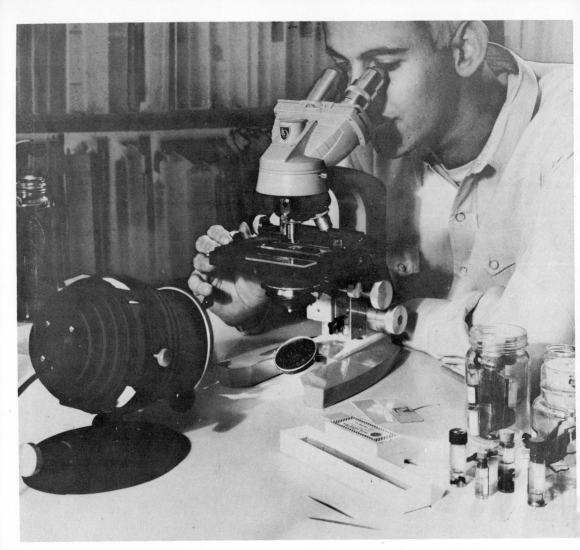

After the specimen is placed on the stage, use the coarse-adjustment knob to bring the objective and the slide as close together as you think necessary to get a clear image. Only then look through the microscope and turn the fine-adjustment knob until the specimen is in sharp focus.

The Insect

What shall we look at first with our microscope? Living things are the most interesting. But which? There is one type of small living thing that we all know, and as it happens these animals also are just the right size for your microscope. We call them insects. We have seen them wherever we go—in the country, on the seashore, and at home. They have tickled and bitten us. We have admired the beauty of some and have been astonished at the oddness of others. Let us start with them in our exploration of the unseen world around us.

Animal life is divided into groups. There is one large group called *arthropods,* which means "jointed legs." As well as having jointed legs, arthropods have a body divided into parts. They have no interior skeleton, but a hard outer covering that varies in shape in accordance with the species to which they belong.

This is the largest of all animal groups. Uncountable billions of arthropods are born and die every year. They exist all over the world and under all kinds of conditions.

The arthropods are divided into several branches. In one branch are such animals as spiders, ticks, and scorpions; another contains the centipedes, and still another the lobsters. In these branches the animal may have many legs: the spider has eight, the lobster has ten with one pair shaped like claws, and the centipede has at least thirty. Some have no feelers and others, such as lobsters, have two pairs.

The animals of another branch are called *insects.* In this branch we find such creatures as the butterfly, moth, beetle, common housefly, and grasshopper.

23

There are over six hundred thousand species of insects. A species is a group of animals or plants which have some things in common and which can transmit these distinctions to their offspring. To separate each species of insect from another, a classification is made according to whether they have wings (and how many and what kind), whether they chew or suck their food, and many other characteristics.

Before becoming a full-grown insect, some of them change from the egg into other forms and structures. This is called a *metamorphosis,* which means a transformation. The complete cycle of metamorphosis in most insects has four stages—the egg, larva, pupa, and adult.

Every insect has its beginning in an egg. The female insect lays eggs. The egg hatches into a larva. Some insects in the larva stage, such as the caterpillar, have legs; others, such as the grub of a beetle, are wormlike. When the larva is full-grown it forms a protective covering and changes into a pupa. The covering is known as a cocoon, a chrysalis, or a pupa case. The adult insect bursts from the cocoon, unfurls its wings, if any, and is ready to mate. The whole process begins again.

The structure of the grasshopper is typical of most insects. It consists of three main parts: the head (1), the thorax (2), and the abdomen (3). The head has a pair of antennae (4), or feelers, one pair of compound eyes (5), and a mouth (6). The thorax is between the head and the abdomen and is made up of three segments to which are attached the wings (7) and the legs (8), three on each side.

The abdomen has eleven or less segments in which are the heart, the stomach, and other organs. On the sides of the thorax and the abdomen are small oval holes (9) through which

the insect breathes. At the end of the abdomen in the female insect is the egg-laying apparatus (10).

Before capturing and looking at insects under the microscope, watch them in their natural surroundings. See how they walk, crawl, jump, fly, and eat. Then examine insects under the microscope and you will understand how they use each part of their body. Your reward will be a thrilling glimpse of the complex structure of a tiny animal which makes it strong despite its small size. The adult life of most insects lasts only a few days or weeks, yet their ancestors inhabited the earth millions of years before the development of man. Many insect species are constantly at war with us. Flies, mosquitoes, lice, fleas, and plant pests attack man, his domestic animals, or his crops—and sometimes win the battle. Other species of insects, however, are beneficial. The honeybee, for example, is essential for the cross-pollination of numerous kinds of plants, including many food crops. Some species help man by preying on insect pests, and others serve as the food of birds and other animals. A number of products made by insects, such as silk fibers and honey, are useful to us. The insect is a remarkable little animal.

25

The Eggs of Insects

Where does an insect come from? Let us watch the beginning of an insect's life.

Put a slice of tomato in a semi-dark but warm place where flies will come. In a day or two you will notice that a grayish white mass begins to grow on its surface. This is called a fungus, which we will study later. Look closely at this growth with your magnifier and you will see little white spots within the mass. Cut out this portion, place it on a slide, and study it under the microscope. They are the eggs of flies, such as those shown in the picture.

All animals, including insects as we have seen, produce eggs. An egg is a single cell of life surrounded with food material and enclosed within a thin membrane or a shell. A chicken egg contains a yolk in which is the living cell. Surrounding the yolk is the albumin, or white of the egg, and this is the food for the living cell which develops into the chicken. Many insect eggs are so tiny that they can be seen only under the microscope. Others, however, are larger and clearly visible. One female insect may lay several hundred eggs. A queen bee may lay as many as two thousand in one day!

During summer days insect eggs can be found everywhere. Butterflies lay their eggs on leaves. Mosquitoes deposit them on water. Many beetles deposit their eggs in decaying wood. Many flies lay their eggs on decaying animal and vegetable matter. The grasshopper digs a hole in the ground and deposits eggs in it, then covers the hole with a sticky substance. Queen bees lay their eggs in the cells of a honeycomb inside a hive.

26

Housefly eggs viewed through the microscope.

Some of these eggs become workers; some develop into male bees and others become queens.

Collect, study, and observe the eggs of different insects. Then you will begin to understand the first part of an insect's life.

The Offspring of Insects

The offspring of most insects are called larvae. We have all seen them. Caterpillars are the larvae of butterflies and moths. Maggots are the larvae of flies. Grubs are the larvae of beetles.

Some insects, such as the locusts, grasshoppers, and crickets, do not have a complete metamorphosis. These baby insects are called *nymphs* and have no wings. As the baby insects get larger they grow wings too. When their wings are full-grown they are adults.

An insect may be a larva for a short or long time, depending on the species. Most insect eggs hatch quickly. If you watch fly eggs very closely every few hours you may see some of them hatch. A small, white, wormlike animal, called a maggot, will come creeping out of the egg. The maggot of the fly lives about four days before it changes into the adult fly. The nymph of the cicada lives underground for seventeen years before it emerges as the adult insect.

Unlike the children of most animals, larvae do not resemble their parents. The larva of a pretty butterfly may be a thin, wormlike caterpillar. A beautiful larva may become a grayish plain-looking moth.

In most species the female dies shortly after she has produced eggs. The mother places her eggs in a spot where the larvae emerging from the eggs can easily find food. They spend an active childhood growing bigger and bigger by eating almost continuously. Social insects, such as the ants, the termites, and some bees and wasps, live in communities. The larvae of these

Caterpillars are the larvae of butterflies and moths.

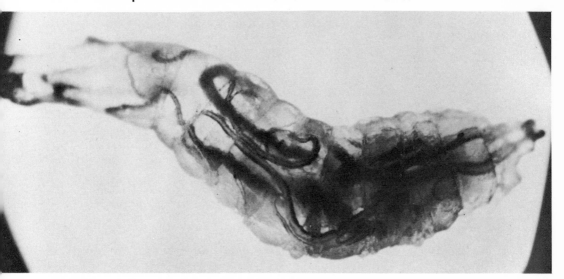

Maggot of a housefly. Because its skin is transparent, the inner structure is revealed by the microscope.

insects are cared for by the workers of the community, which has a long-lived, egg-laying female called the queen.

Where do the larva of the solitary insects live? Everywhere. Not many stay where they are hatched, but move toward places of food and safety. Caterpillars are found on the leaves and stems of plants and trees, where they nibble the vegetation thoroughly. Many grubs dig themselves into the ground and live at the roots of plants.

In early summer, on the stems of trees and rocks, we can find a small frothy mass known as frog spit. This is the nest of a small insect called a frog hopper. If you disturb the spit, you will find tiny larvae in its center. Other insects live their larva stage in flowing water or, as in the case of the mosquito, in stagnant water.

While the insect is undergoing this stage of its life cycle, it is nearly helpless against its enemies. It cannot run or fly away. We all have seen caterpillars that rise up and wriggle about when disturbed. Others have little horns which they wave in a threatening manner as if they were ready to fight. Some caterpillars give off a disagreeable odor when they are frightened. Others play dead and assume positions which make them identical with their surroundings. By this means, many escape the notice of their most voracious enemy, the bird.

The food of the larvae is as varied as that of the insects. Many eat the fresh leaves of plants. Some only suck plant juices. Others live on decaying vegetable matter and some use the dead and decaying flesh of animals as their food source. But no matter what larvae eat, they all eat continuously and in enormous quantities. They grow large and become fat rapidly. Their fat is stored up as a food supply for the final change toward be-

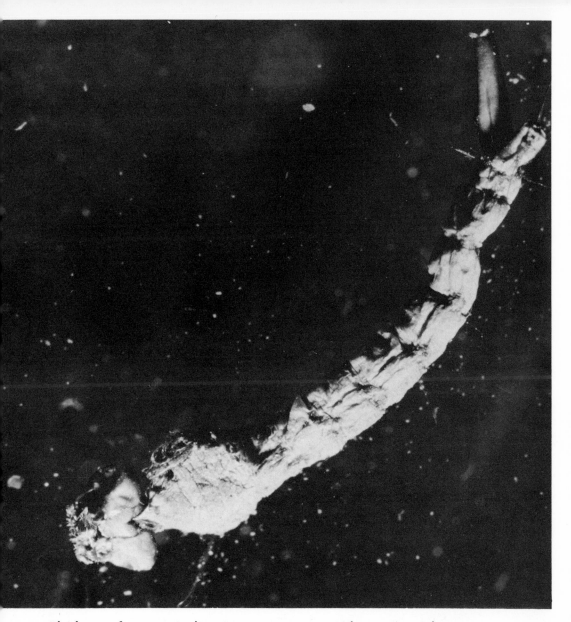

The larva of a mosquito lives in stagnant water. When at rest, it hangs downward from the water surface, breathing through the little tube shown at upper right. Oil poured on the water will shut off the air supply for the larva.

coming adults. Some grow so quickly that their skin becomes too small, and every few days they shed it and emerge with a brand-new one. The fly larva does this three times.

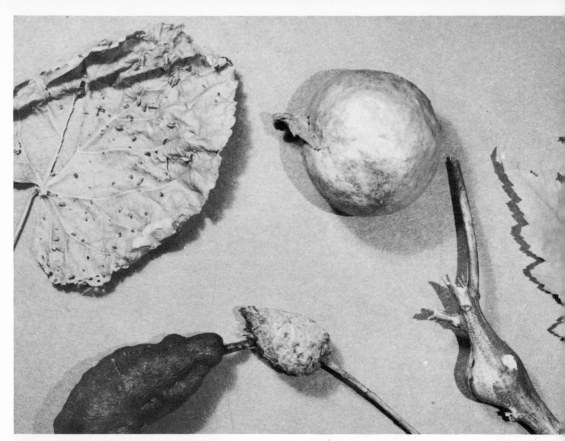

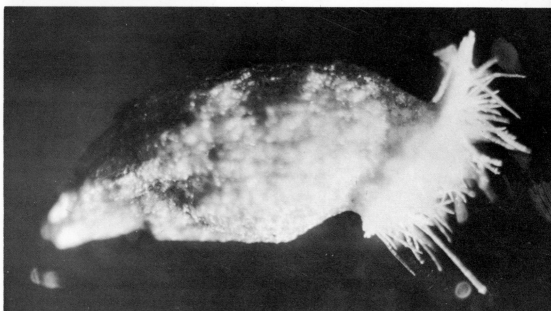

Top: All the swellings and spots are galls made on different plants by the larvae of various gall insects. Bottom: A view through the microscope of one of the galls from the leaf shown at upper left.

During a walk in the woods have you noticed little knobby objects on leaves and branches? Sometimes the leaves of a young oak tree are thickly covered with them. They feel strangely hard in comparison to the soft pulpy leaf. These hard swellings are called galls and are caused by insects. Galls are found in three forms: round, button-shaped, and rose-shaped. If you open one of them carefully you will find one or more small larvae inside.

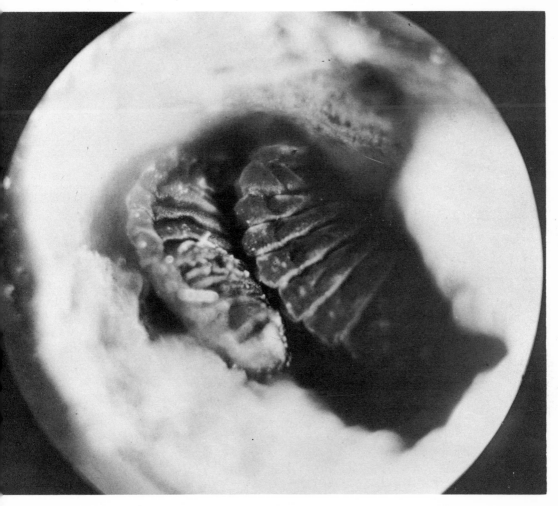

Gall larvae inside a gall.

Certain flies, moths, or wasps called gall insects take care of their young in an interesting and curious manner. The insect lays an egg on the leaf or branch. When the larva hatches out of the egg, it irritates the plant in some way. Exactly how this is done is not known. The plant cells around the larva begin to grow fast and beyond their normal size until the larva is entirely covered by this abnormal growth.

After some time the larvae of all insects stop eating. Some travel away from the neighborhood where they have been during most of their life. You may have seen a great many caterpillars on a country road at one time. They all seem to be looking for something.

When they have found the place they are searching for, some larvae take leaves and fasten them with silk thread to the branches of trees. Then they wrap themselves in the leaves, fastening the edges and the tops and bottoms together with more silk thread. Others begin to spin a continuous thread of silk around themselves until they are completely encased and drop to the ground where they lie still among the dead leaves. Others creep into the small cracks of tree stems, into the hollows of rocks, underneath stones, or into the joints of fences, and then close up the entrance with a thick and tight silk door. There are larvae which attach themselves to the stems of water plants underneath the water, and, after piercing the stem so that they can breathe the air that enters the stem from above, spin a silk covering about themselves. Others dig themselves deep into the ground and then close their cave with a silk curtain.

When the larva achieves this stage of life, it sheds its skin once more. During this period from which it will emerge as an

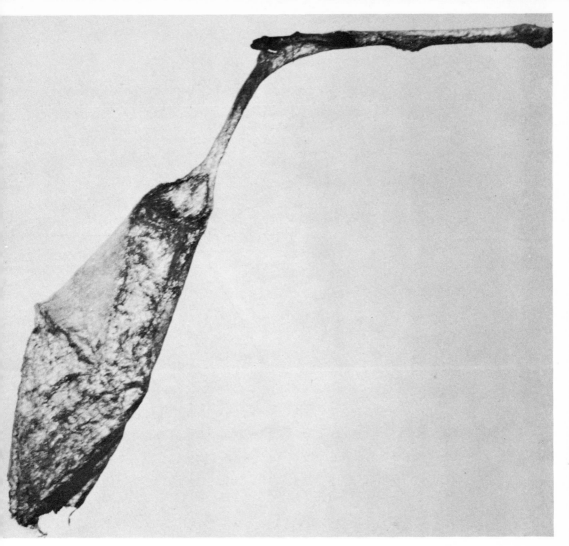

A cocoon wrapped in a leaf hanging from a branch of a tree.

adult, the insect is called a pupa, and the nest the larva has made is called a cocoon.

The silk of a cocoon is made from a liquid coming out of an opening in the body of the larva. When the liquid reaches the air it hardens into the fibrous material that we call silk. Even though the silk may remain exposed to the air for many months,

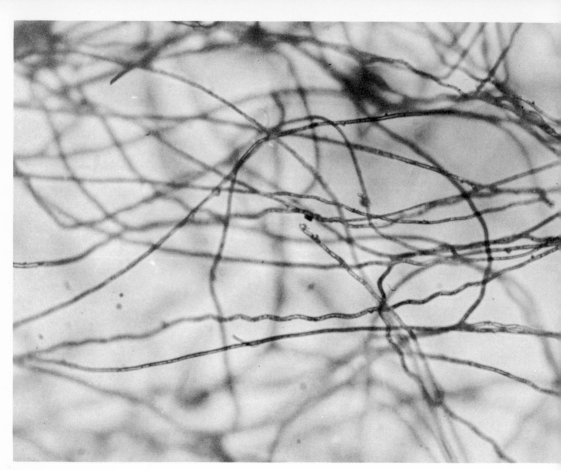

When a piece of the outside covering of a cocoon is viewed under the microscope, it shows that the cocoon is made of fine silky threads.

it aways remains sticky, so that on the slightest touch any object, if not too large, will stick to the cocoon.

Silk spinning is a unique method of protection. A pupa would be helpless against weather and enemies were it not for the silken covering, the cocoon.

The period in which an insect remains a pupa may be only a few weeks for certain insects, or an entire winter for others. One kind of butterfly has two generations every summer. The first generation lays its eggs in the spring and the pupae of these eggs become full-fledged insects late in the summer.

However, the pupae from the eggs of those late-summer butter-flies remain in their cocoons during the entire winter.

When the insect is in the pupa stage a remarkable transformation in its structure takes place. It remains absolutely motionless within its cocoon and gives no visible signs of life. Yet, during this period, the entire body of the pupa is transformed until it begins to resemble the insect. When it has reached that stage, it emerges from the cocoon and flies away as a full-grown insect.

In early autumn collect as many cocoons as you can find. Examine some of them very carefully. Notice how they' are constructed. Keep others in a cool place and in spring watch the insect emerge.

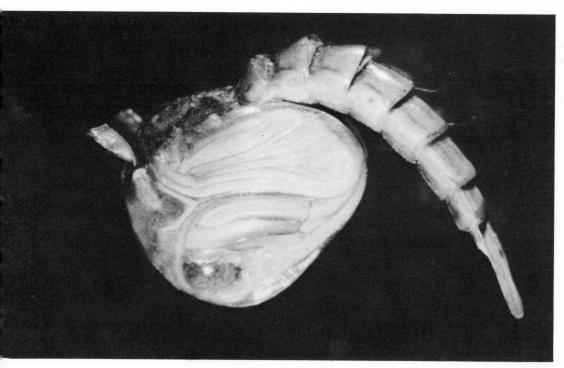

The pupa of a mosquito.

How the Insect Eats

Despite its small size, the insect requires a large amount of food. Its diet is simple and there is generally plenty for it to eat.

The butterfly flits over the sunny field choosing the flower among thousands from which it will sip nectar. The bee busily collects pollen and nectar from many kinds of plants. The grasshopper explores his rich storehouse of food among the grasses. The fly hovers about the outside of a screen door knowing that patience and persistence may get him in. An insect is always hungry. Its stomach always wants food.

The mouth of an insect is efficiently made for what it has to do. Each species of insect has a mouth adapted to the kind of food the insect eats. Certain insects chew solid food and others sip liquid.

The mouth of a grasshopper is typical of the chewing insect. It is on the underside of its head, and has two lips, upper and lower. When the upper lip is carefully removed by cutting it away, two surfaces may be seen, one on each side of the mouth. These are called the *mandibles,* and they are the chewing and grinding apparatus which functions as do our jaws. When the insect eats, the mandibles move from side to side. This is opposite to the action of our jaws, which move mainly up and down. Remove the mandibles of the grasshopper carefully with a pin by bending them backward and study their shape under the microscope. Compare them with the mandibles of other insects in size and shape.

When the lower lip is carefully removed, the tongue can be seen. Remove the tongue and study it under the microscope.

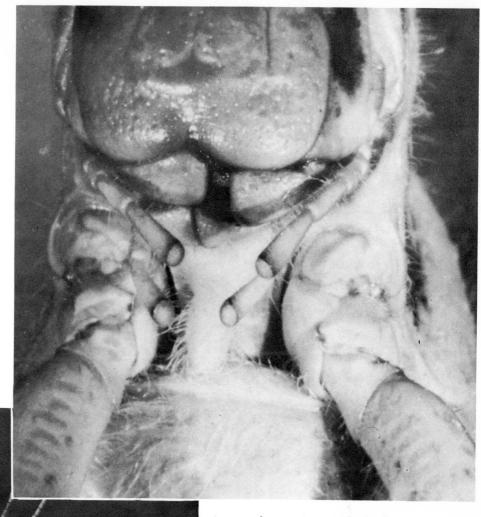

A grasshopper's mouth (indicated at left by the arrow) is shown greatly magnified to reveal the mandibles and maxillae used in biting and chewing.

In the back of the cavity created by the removal of these organs, you will find a pair of jaws called the *maxillae*, which move sidewise, as do the mandibles. From these upper maxillae there extend outward two segmented sections which look somewhat like feelers. They are named *palps*. The lower two maxillae are fused together and form the lower lip. They also have palps but are much smaller.

In eating, the mandibles and the maxillae work together in tearing the food to a convenient size for swallowing. The palps are used for touching and probably for smelling the food about to be consumed.

There are many insects that cannot eat unless the food is in liquid form. The fly, for instance, does not eat solid food. When you see it on solids such as sugar, it is sponging up moisture from the food, which it has mixed with its saliva. Sucking insects have palps that are stunted or not visible.

The mouth of such insects which is called the *proboscis*, extends downward from the head. When not in use, it is either raised or coiled spirally under the head. The proboscis is a marvelous structure composed of two parts, each covered with many fine hairs. These two parts clinging together form a hollow groove or tube which is used for sucking food. In the bee the tip of the proboscis is circular and concave, and resembles a small spoon. The edges of this spoon have branched hairs for gathering food from flowers.

Some insects can pierce the covering over their food. The mosquito does not really bite, but pierces the skin to suck up blood. Some types of insects, such as the mayfly, do not eat at all when they are fully grown, and therefore the mouth is greatly underdeveloped.

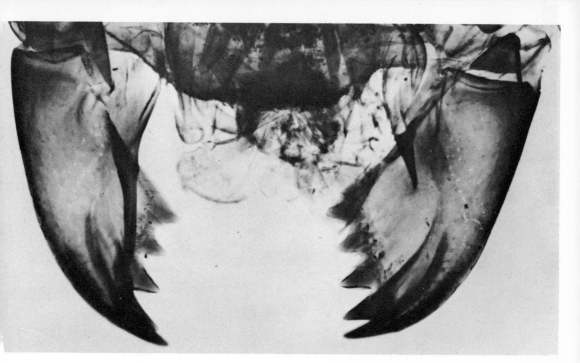

The mouth of an ant. The mandibles shown large above can be seen at lower part of head below.

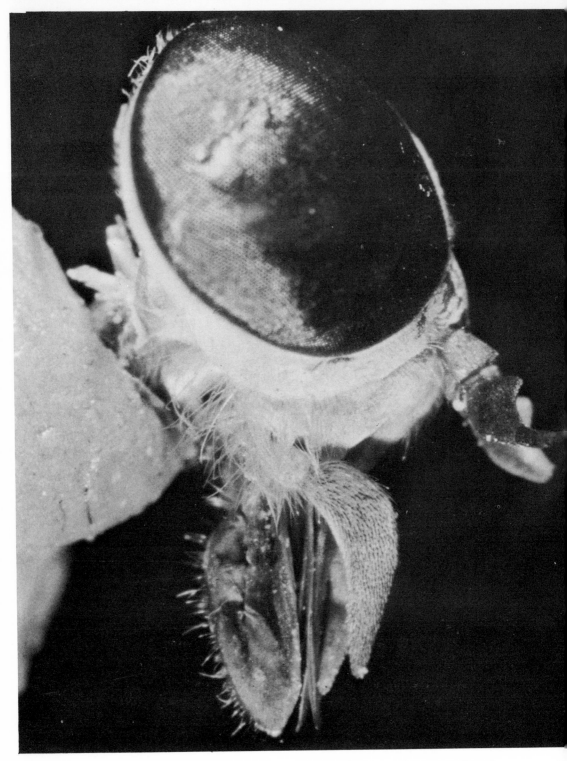

Proboscis of a horsefly extending downward from its head.

Proboscis of a butterfly coiled in a spiral under its head.

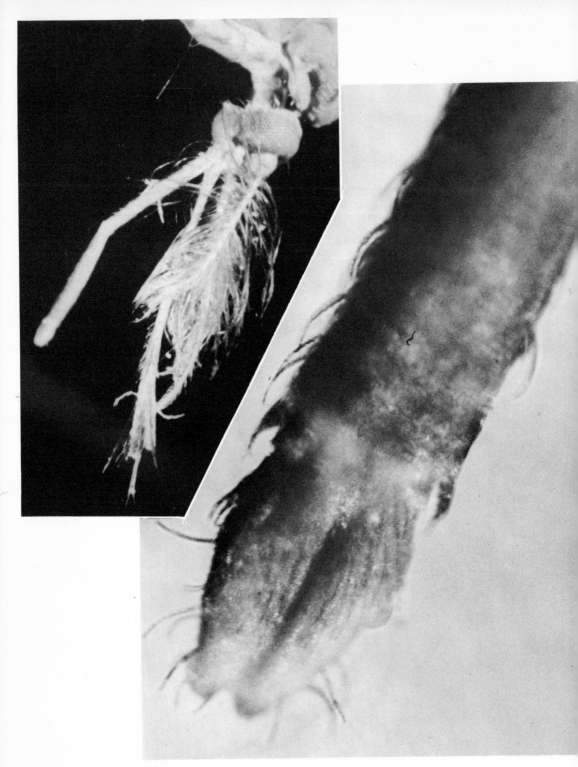

Proboscis of a mosquito, with a greatly magnified view of the part that pierces the skin to obtain blood.

How the Insect Feels

The feelers, or *antennae,* of an insect are its hands. It uses them to touch things. Some insects may also smell with their antennae, and others hear with them.

Near the top of the head of every insect there is one pair of antennae. Each antenna is divided into little joints so that it can bend smoothly and easily in every direction. Some insects have only two joints in each antenna, but others have as many as eighty.

There are as many different varieties of antennae as there are species of insects. Some are long and slender, others are short and stubby. Some are smooth and bare, but those of such insects as the large night-flying moths branch out to form a fine feathery bush. The ends of antennae also differ. In some insects the antenna comes to a fine point and in others, such as the butterfly, it ends in a little knob.

Each insect takes good care of its antennae. When they become soiled, the insect carefully washes them with its mouth or strokes them with its legs to clean them.

Watch an insect to discover how it uses its antennae. Compare the antennae of a grasshopper or an ant with those of a night-flying moth or a butterfly. Studying the antennae under the microscope, you can count the number of joints in each variety. You can examine the intricate structure of a feathered antenna.

Antennae of a grasshopper.

Each antenna of this butterfly has a small knoblike end.

A large moth, which has feather-like antennae. A photomicrograph of its antenna appears as the first picture in this book.

How the Insect Sees

At each side of the insect head is a very large oval eye. In some insects these eyes take up most of the head. Each large oval eye is called a compound eye, because it is made up of many small eyes. The insect cannot move the small ones about, as we do ours, nor does it have eyelids. The compound eyes are so placed that the insect can see all around it. No matter from what direction you try to catch a fly, its eyes can see your approaching hand.

The number of small eyes varies according to the species. Some of the smaller creeping insects have very few in each compound eye. The flying insects have the most eyes of all; there is one moth that is said to have twenty-seven thousand. Most insects also have several single eyes on the top or in front of the head between the compound eyes.

With so many eyes, how does the insect see? Every eye sends a separate image to the brain. Each image is very small, but where the range of vision for one eye ends, another begins, and so on. The result is that the insect sees a scene as many little pictures, one next to another, forming a complete picture of what is around it.

Study the eyes of a moth, a grasshopper, a fly and other insects under the microscope.

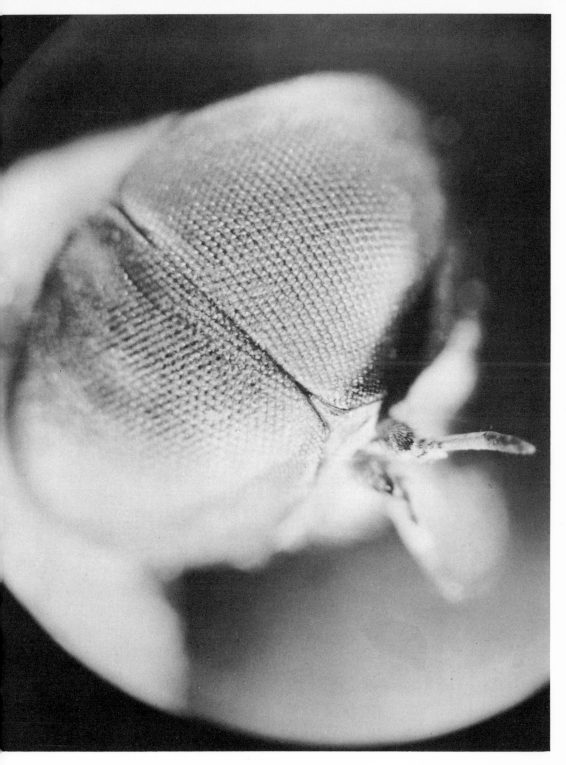

The compound eyes of a large fly.

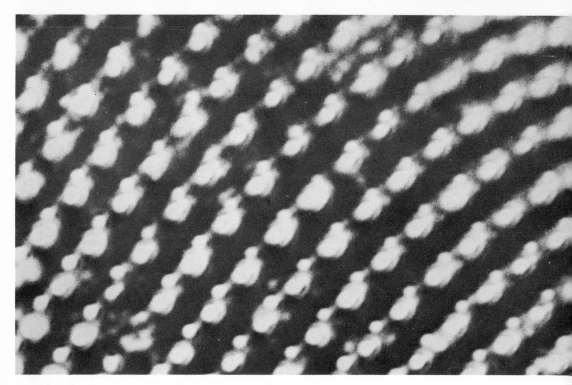

A section of the fly's compound eye. Each white spot is one eye.

The single eyes on the top of the fly's head.

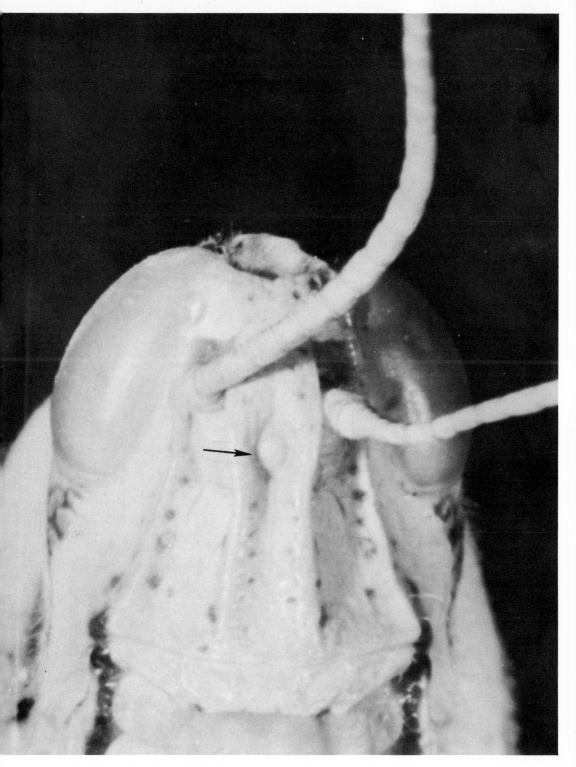

A single eye (indicated by the arrow) on the head of a grasshopper.

How the Insect Walks

Some lazy summer afternoon sit down near an ant colony and watch how the ants run busily back and forth along their paths. See how sure-footed they are. Nothing in their path will stop them from going about their work. They will climb nimbly over a twig that must appear to them as big as a tree trunk does to us. No matter how large the food burden they are carrying to their nest, they plod along untiringly. Hour after hour they travel back and forth between the food source and their nest, foraging for provisions without rest.

An insect has six legs, never more or less. They are used principally for walking, but some insects use them for other purposes as well. Looking at an insect's leg under the microscope will show you how it is constructed. The leg is divided into five main parts. The part closest to the body holds the leg in place and can move the entire leg freely. A smaller part below connects it with the thigh, which in turn is connected with the shin. Below the shin is the foot, which itself may be divided into several parts, sometimes as many as five. At the end of the foot there are small claws surrounding a soft cushion which has a number of fine sticky hairs that enable the insect to walk up a wall or on a ceiling. To prevent the cushion from being damaged, the insect raises it when walking on an uneven surface.

In the picture of a fly's leg notice the cushion in the lower part. When a fly alights upon any unclean substance, some of it will stick to the hairs of the cushion, and later the insect may deposit this filth on our food.

The leg of a fly.

The soft, moist, flexible under-
pad of the fly's foot.

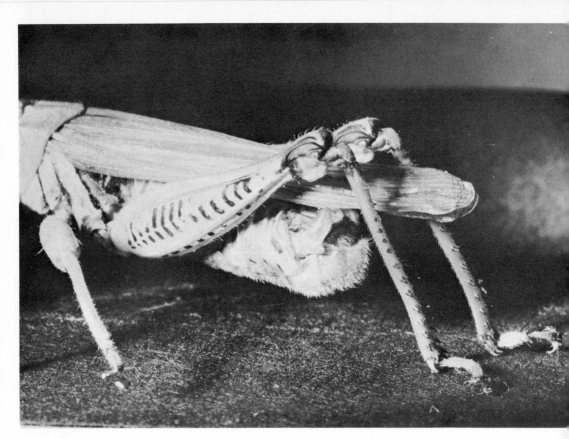

The strong rear legs of a grasshopper.

The size and shape of the front and back pairs of legs vary in different insects. The grasshopper uses its strongly developed rear legs for jumping. It would be fun to measure the jump of a grasshopper and then, after comparing the size and weight of a grasshopper to those of a man, to calculate how far or high a man would have to jump to equal it. The legs of some insects are adapted for swimming; the center and rear legs of the water boatman, for instance, are flattened out and serve as oars. The bee uses its hairy back legs for collecting food from flowers.

There are beetles which clean their antennae by means of a brush of hair that grows on their legs. Beetles which burrow

Above: The oar-shaped leg of a water boatman. Below: In the water boatman the small legs nearest the head are used for grasping food and the middle and hind legs are developed for swimming.

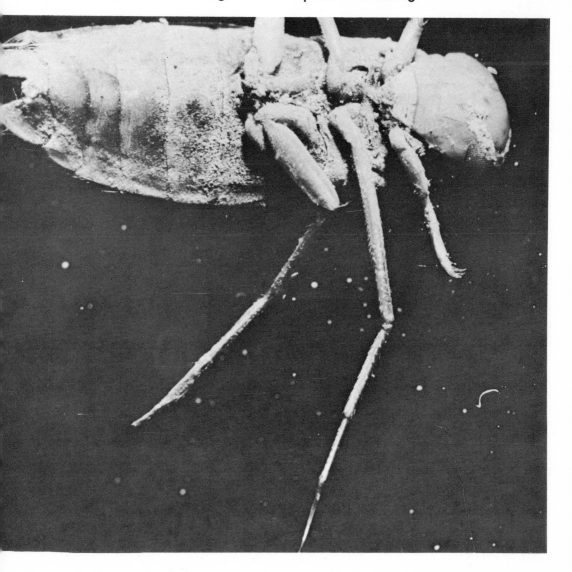

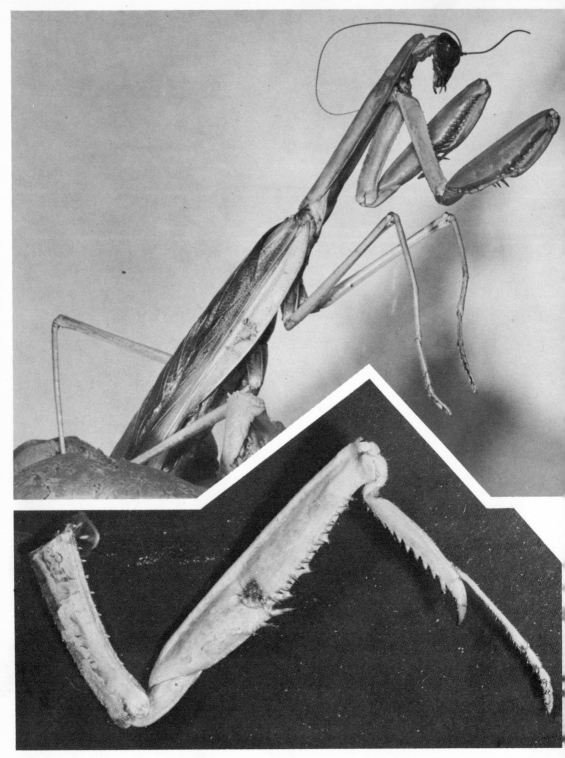

The praying mantis has specialized front legs. Part of the leg has developed into a clawlike structure used for capturing prey.

underground have very wide front legs for digging; others have long and powerful front legs for climbing on trees.

The praying mantis, the largest insect of all and very important to us as a destroyer of many harmful insects, has well-developed front legs which are used as weapons of attack. The illustration shows part of one of those legs. With such weapons the mantis can pounce upon its prey, and once in those clutches the prey is powerless.

The front legs of many butterflies are so small that the insect can hardly use them. The gnat has very long, slender legs.

With three pairs of legs, how does the insect walk and run? It moves the first and third leg on one side together with the center leg on the other side. This combination gives it a firm triangular support while it moves the other legs forward for a similar stance.

The fore wings of a butterfly are larger than its rear wings.

How the Insect Flies

Almost all kinds of insects have wings, which vary greatly in appearance, size, and structure, depending on the species.

The wing is a membrane, or skin, attached to the thorax. Each membrane is strengthened by hollow rods which branch out from the thorax and extend to the edge of the wing. These rods are called veins. The branching of veins distinguishes, in many cases, one species of insect from another.

In some insects, such as the grasshopper and beetle, the fore wings are very hard and form a covering for the protection of the smaller rear wings. The butterfly has two large fore wings and two smaller rear wings. The fly has only two wings; in place of the rear wings are two little knobs called stabilizers.

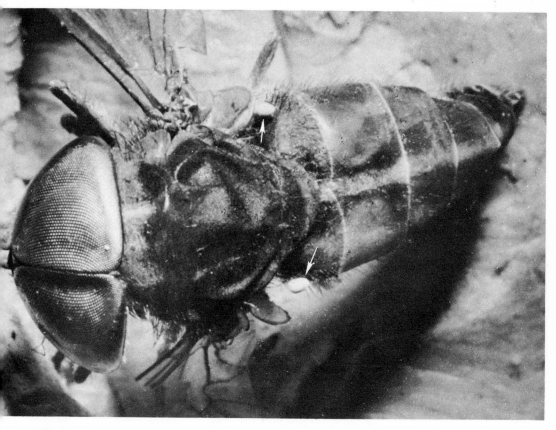

The two small white ovals (indicated by arrows) are the fly's stabilizers, which enable it to change its direction instantly in flight.

Wing of a housefly. Notice the strong hairs on the outer edge of the wing and the smaller hairs of the membrane between the veins.

The wings of many insects are covered by hairs. In some insects, such as butterflies and moths, these hairs are flat and are called scales. The absolutely regular pattern with which scales cover the wings of the insect is marvelous. When a few of these scales are removed carefully, one can study the manner in which they are fastened to the wing. (See page 147.)

When an insect is at rest, the wings recline in different ways, according to the species. The butterfly keeps its wings upright while resting on a flower. The moth slopes its wings downward like the sloping roof of a house. The fly rests its wings level with its body.

A few insects use their wings to make sounds. Some locusts rub their hind legs against the fore wings. Others, such as the katydid, rub their fore wings together. Others make a crackling sound when flying by rubbing together the under surface of the fore wing and the upper and frontal part of the rear wing. Some insects, such as the ants and termites, use the wings only during the mating flight and to establish a new nest, and then drop or gnaw off their wings after one flight.

Even though the wings of most insects seem very delicate, they are wonderfully constructed for hard work. When studying the wings of insects under the microscope you will discover how they are strengthened by the veins and by their attachment to the thorax. Compare the vein structure of the wings of butter-flies and flies.

The remarkable strength and endurance of any insect can be seen in the speed with which it flies and the long time it remains in the air. Some insects, such as the dragonfly, are as swift as a swallow. Untiringly, hour after hour, they dart rapidly back and forth to catch those insects upon which they feed. The

A mosquito's wing.

Dragonfly resting on a leaf.

rapidity with which an insect waves its wings up and down is quite astonishing. The bee can make one hundred and ninety strokes of its wings every second. The fly is even faster; it moves its wings about three hundred times a second.

Many insects use their wings not only for flying but also as protection against enemies. The wings of many moths resting against the trunk of a tree look exactly like the sun-streaked bark, and cannot be distinguished by birds or other enemies. There are butterflies with wings resembling in color and shape the leaves of trees. Grasshoppers have brightly colored rear wings which can be seen only in flight; the front wings are spotted in dull shades of brown and green. When at rest, the grasshopper folds its front wings over the rear wings and immediately blends with the landscape.

Camouflage by matching the colors of the environment is highly developed among many insects. Scientists call it protective coloration, because the insect thus escapes being detected and eaten by its enemies.

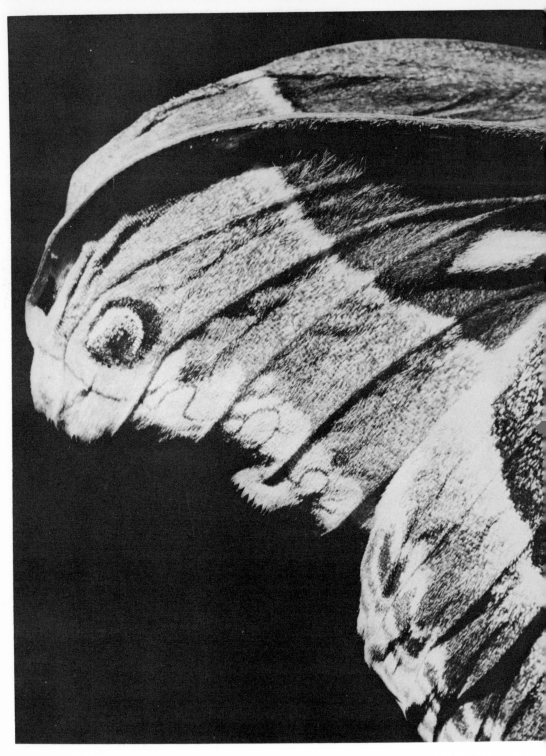

A section of a moth's wing. Its coloration and markings are similar to those of the tree trunks on which the moth rests.

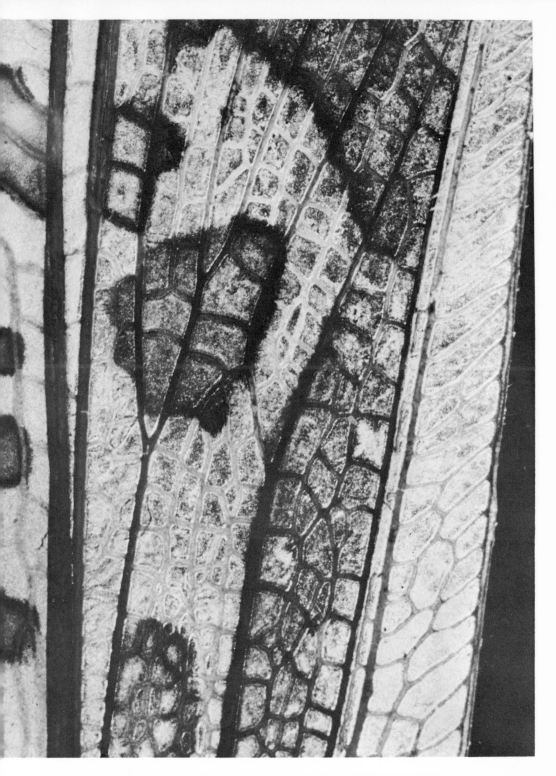

A section of the outer wing of a grasshopper. The hard, leathery surface has a color pattern which blends into the landscape.

The body of this butterfly has a mottled coloring which helps to make it invisible to its enemies, the birds.

There are certain butterflies and moths which are not good for birds to eat. The wings of these insects are marked with conspicuous designs of bright colors, and birds seeing such a color pattern avoid eating them. Some other butterflies and moths, though harmless to birds, have wings closely resembling those of the harmful ones, and hence the birds shun them also. Similarity in the appearance of a harmless insect to a dangerous one is called mimicry.

66

The Fly

One of the most numerous of all insects is the fly. Flies are found in nearly every part of the world. The different species vary in size from small ones that can be seen only under the microscope to giants about two inches long. Flies differ from most other flying insects in having only two useful wings.

The common housefly is the most familiar to us. It has four black bands on the back of the thorax. The housefly breeds very rapidly in decaying animal and vegetable matter. A fly lives only about two weeks, but in that short time one female can produce so many eggs that, were they all to hatch and become flies, within five months her descendants would number about five billion!

Fortunately the fly has many enemies; among them are spiders, ants, centipedes, the praying mantis, frogs, and chickens, all of which prey upon flies. We prevent the housefly from multiplying by using insecticides and by sanitation.

The fly feeds on every kind of animal and vegetable food. It is a very dangerous insect because it carries bacteria and other microorganisms that cause disease in man and domestic animals.

Study all kinds of flies. Watch how they move about when in flight and at rest, and notice how they feed. Compare the wings, eyes, and head structure of various flies under the microscope.

A worker ant forages diligently to keep its colony supplied with food.

The Ant

The ants are one of the oldest groups of animals in existence. Eight species still very busy in our forests today are known to have existed fifty million years ago.

Ants live in highly organized communities. Their colonies might well be called cities, as many of them contain hundreds of thousands of individuals.

The inhabitants of a colony are divided into three chief classes: males, females or queens, and workers. Certain species have a fourth class called "soldier ants," which protect the colony from enemies.

Some ants capture the colony of another species and carry off its eggs. The ants hatched from these become slaves and work for their masters.

The ants of each colony have a characteristic odor. No matter how large the colony may be, an ant always recognizes a fellow member by smell if they meet outside their nest. An ant with a different odor is instantly known as a stranger and is attacked.

Ants feed on both vegetable and animal matter. Some ants even have domestic animals. From the bodies of small insects, known as aphids, or plant lice, oozes a sweet liquid which the ants use as food. During the winter, in the underground colony, the ant tends the eggs of this insect very carefully until they hatch. In spring, they carry the young aphids to the plants upon which these insects feed. Indeed, the ants care for their domestic insects as a farmer cares for his cows, protecting them and taking them to good feeding places.

The workers of many species of ants are highly specialized for specific jobs. One species grows its own food. Certain workers go into the forest to cut fresh leaves from trees and carry them back to the colony. A second group chews up these leaves to prepare a culture bed in an underground chamber. On these prepared leaves a third group grows small mushrooms which are used by the colony for food.

These are just a few examples of the amazing accomplishments of the ant communities.

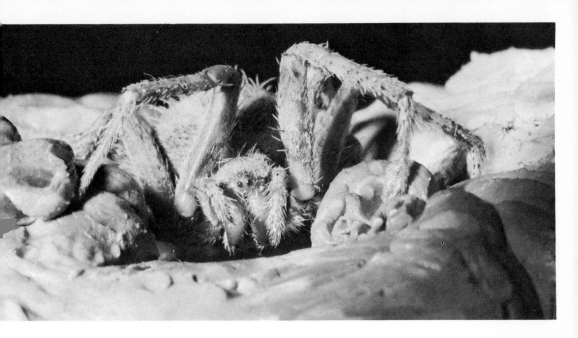

The Spider

The spider is not an insect. Its head is not separate from the thorax and it has eight single eyes and no antennae or jaw, such as those of insects. The spider is an eight-legged arthropod belonging to the group called *Arachnida*.

Spiders live everywhere from the high mountains to the seashore. They are hunters and trappers, and they feed on insects. Some pounce on or run after their prey; others spin webs to trap it. The spider takes only liquid food; it sucks the juices of the insects with its mouth, while holding the prey in the claws of its two front legs.

The most outstanding feature of the spider is its ability to spin enormous quantities of silk, which it uses to build webs for capturing its prey or to construct various sorts of shelters and abodes, including cocoons for its eggs and young. It is the only

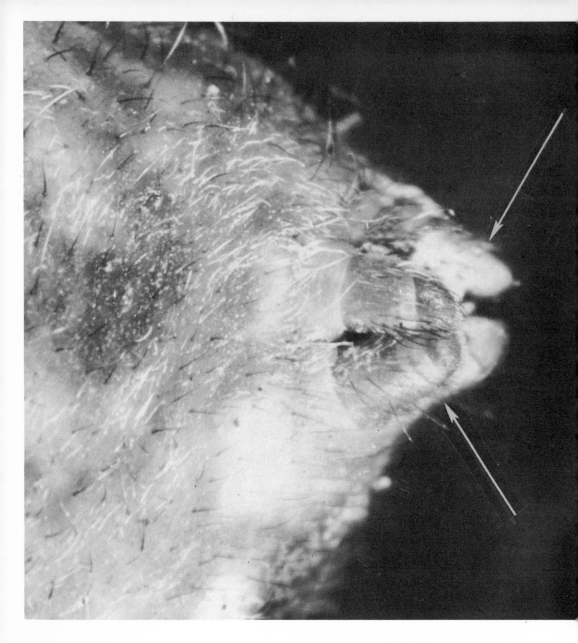

The spinnerets, viewed from the side.

animal that spins silk during its adult life. At the back of the
abdomen are small tubes, the spinnerets, which eject a liquid
that hardens in the air into fine threads which we call silk. Many
spiders construct silk webs that are marvels of engineering.

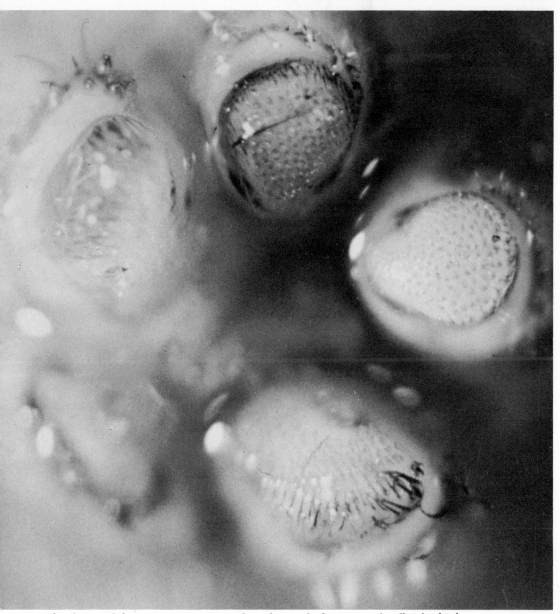

The front of the spinnerets. Out of each tiny hole comes the fluid which hardens in the air to form a thread of spider silk.

The trapdoor spider lives in the ground. Its home has a small hinged door, and when the spider wants food, it opens the door slightly and peers out; then it pounces upon any insect coming within reach.

73

On the spider's foot is a comb used in the construction of its web.

There is a spider which binds several dead leaves together with its silk, making a raft on which it sails across water. Any insect alighting on this pirate raft is attacked by the spider.

When a young spider wants to travel and see the world, it stands high on its legs and releases a fine thread of silk. The wind carries the thread up with the spider attached. Young spiders have been found floating high in the air and over the sea many miles away from land.

The Sponge

The sponge is one of the simplest types of many-celled animals. Because some sponges live together in large colonies, they have a plantlike appearance. The cells are porous, yet their outer coverings are tough and fibrous. A living sponge colony is a dark slimy mass with many small openings, or pores, on the outside for bringing in water, from which it extracts its food and the oxygen required for breathing.

The sponge inside is hollow and lined with cells which have slender whiplike threads that move back and forth, creating a current in the water. When food particles in the water touch these cells, they are sucked in and digested.

Sponges grow and multiply by budding. A young sponge cell grows out of an older one; it may attach itself to the older one or, if carried off by water currents, it may start a new sponge colony somewhere else.

The flexible framework is called spongin. It forms a series of tubes which branch out in all directions. When examined under the microscope, it is seen to be fibrous. In this framework are tiny mineral substances in various beautiful shapes which give rigidity to the sponge mass.

Sponges are distributed over the entire world. Most of them live in salt water along the seacoast, but a few exist in fresh water. All sponges are attached to rocks, wooden piles, old shells, or other solid objects below the water.

Sponge fishermen often cut one sponge colony into many parts, put each part in a favorable place for its growth on the ocean

A sponge colony.

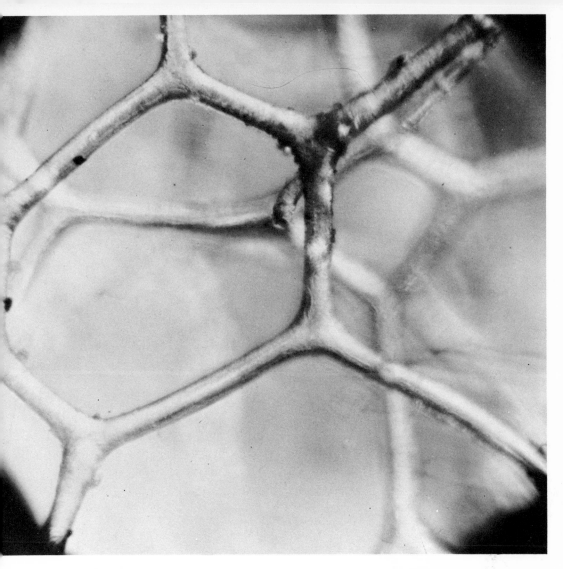

The microscope reveals the porous structure of a sponge skeleton.

floor, and in this manner increase the sponge supply. For commercial use the sponge is cleaned, and only the dried skeleton of the animal is sold. Commercial sponges come from the Mediterranean Sea and from the waters off the Florida coast. Sponges have been used for thousands of years for bathing, cleaning, and drying things.

A man-made sponge.

Recently artificial sponges have been created from chemicals and cellulose, the woody part of plants. These, called viscose sponges, are used for the same purposes as the natural sponge. Thus science imitates and improves on nature.

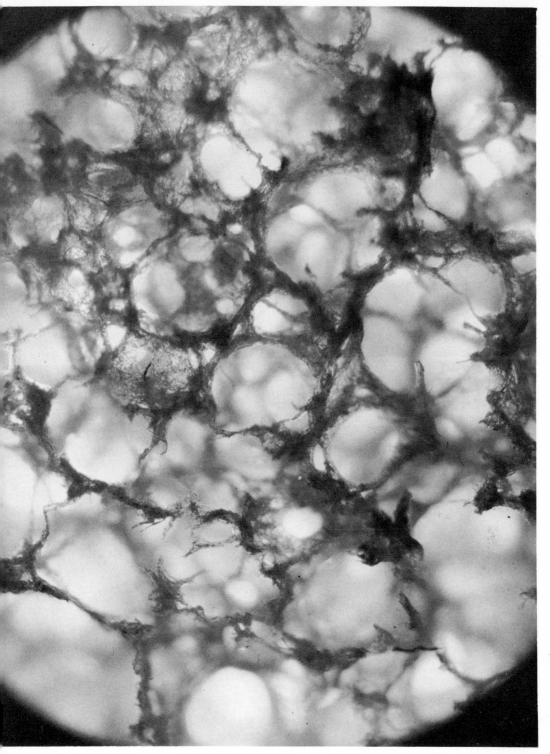

An artificial sponge viewed through the microscope.

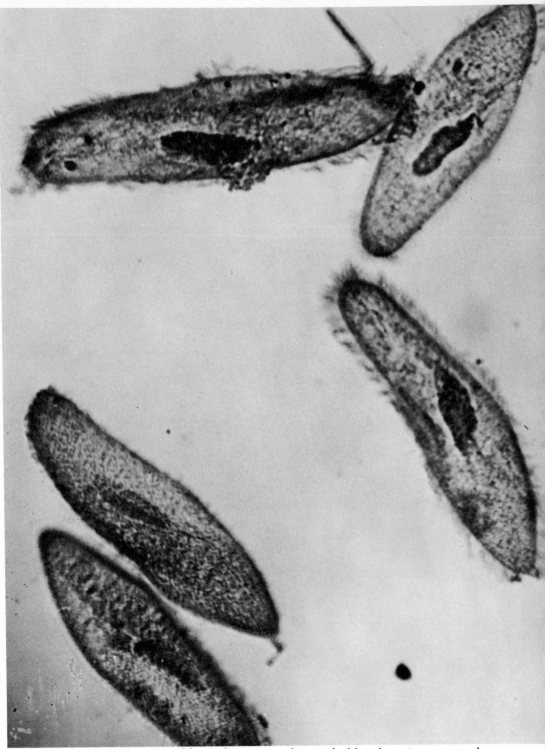

Protozoa. Invisible to the eye until revealed by the microscope, these tiny animals live an active life in water.

The Protozoa

Protozoa seems a strange word when it is encountered for the first time. It is taken from the Greek and means "first animal."

One of the most thrilling experiences is to see protozoa under the microscope. Water from a sea, lake, brook, or river can be used for this purpose, as it contains these creatures in countless numbers. Another method of obtaining protozoa is to boil about a pint of water, cool it, and pour it into a clean jar. Place in this water some plant matter, such as a stem, a lettuce leaf, or a few blades of grass. Let the jar remain at room temperature for at least two days. Place a drop of this liquid, called an infusion, in a cavity slide under the microscope. The infusion will be found to contain many living and active creatures.

The protozoon is a one-celled animal. Its single cell performs all the necessary functions of its body; it has sections for taking in food, for digestion, and for the elimination of waste materials and gases. Protozoa feed by making a current of water flow into them. Any edible substance found in the water, such as bacteria and plant matter, is kept in their bodies to be digested, while the water is ejected. If you watch the protozoa closely, you can observe this remarkable action.

Protozoa have many shapes. A thin membrane holds the cell together. No matter how complex one of these animals may appear, it is only one cell.

Despite their simple structure, the protozoa get along quite well. As you look through your microscope into their world, you see some of them swimming around rapidly or stopping now and

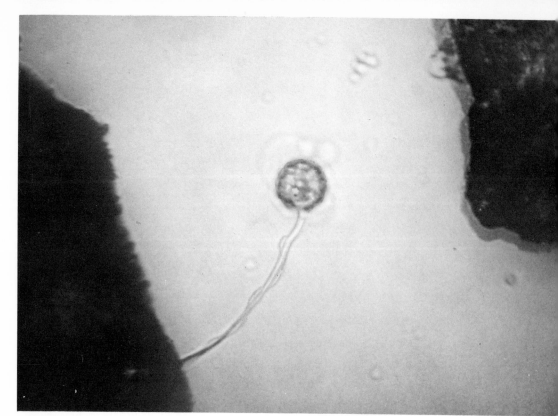

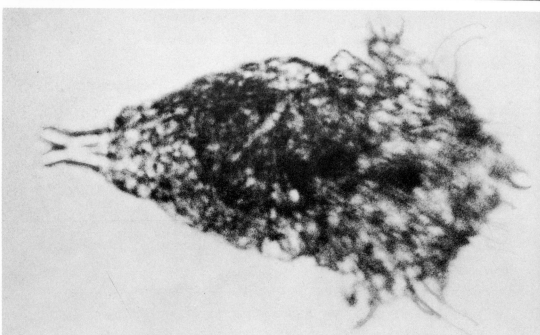

Bewildering forms of life, strange and beautiful, exist in a drop of water. Some resemble a flower fastened by the stalk to a grain of sand, but many others have strange shapes with no resemblance to anything seen outside the world of the microscope.

then to rest or to investigate some decaying vegetable matter for food. Others creep along the bottom of the drop in the cavity slide.

Protozoa are quite transparent and, with moderate magnification, one can see the interiors of their bodies. They are so constantly active that it is advisable to slow them down. Get some quince seeds from the drugstore and soak them in a small amount of water overnight. Next day, if you put a drop of the resulting jelly into the water containing protozoa, it will slow down the movements of the protozoa.

Most protozoa are colorless. One of them, shown in the accompanying illustration, somewhat resembles a flower. It is fastened to a small grain of sand by a stalk that is part of its body. When hunting for food, it stretches itself out from its base and explores the water with a swaying motion. If disturbed, it retracts quicker than a wink and hides itself under the grain of sand, from which a few moments later it cautiously comes forth again.

There are some protozoa which live in the bodies of humans and animals. These species are called parasites because they take their food from the blood stream and other parts of the animal in which they live. Most parasitical protozoa are harmless, but there are some which may cause sickness and even death.

Obtain samples of water from different places and see how many kinds of protozoa you can find. If you are near the ocean, compare the protozoa found in salt water with those in lake and river water.

Make infusions of pieces of dead plants. Study them daily and notice that the number of protozoa increases and also that some grow quite large. As the infusions become older, notice that the number of protozoa in a drop begins to diminish again. This happens when the food supply diminishes and the water becomes too stale for the animals to live in.

The study of protozoa has interested many scientists. Though very small, they are an important link in the chain of the living organisms that inhabit the earth. There are thirty thousand known species of protozoa. These fascinating single-celled animals are found wherever there is water, and anyone who studies them under a microscope will be rewarded with hours of wonderful discoveries.

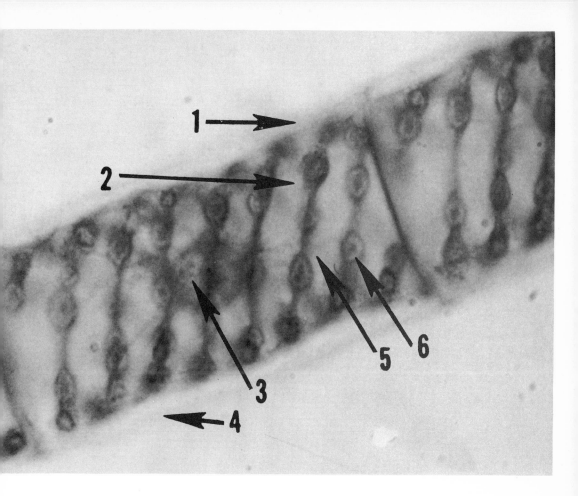

The Cell

The cell is the unit of life. Only cells can make more cells. Only they can combine to make leaves, tree trunks, roots—the whole plant—or to make blood, eyes, legs—the whole animal.

The cell of a single green alga, called *Spirogyra,* shows a typical cell structure. The living cell contains a semi-liquid material called *protoplasm* (1). When we speak of life, we mean protoplasm. It takes food, it grows, it breathes, and by dividing itself it multiplies and builds the tissues.

Within the protoplasm is the *cytoplasm* (2), a granular material which contains many complex substances and a round or oval body called the *nucleus* (3) which controls the activity of the cell.

Within the nucleus are very tiny bodies called *chromosomes.* They are so small that their fine structure can be seen clearly only by using an electron microscope, which provides much greater magnification than the most powerful optical microscope. Since all cells seem so much alike, how is it that a geranium cell will always make a geranium plant and a cat cell will always make a cat? The chromosomes bear the fundamental units of heredity, known as the *genes,* which may be called the "cell memory." The genes in the cell of a geranium plant "remember" that the cell came from a geranium and they activate the cell to build a geranium and nothing else.

A space in the cell is called the *vacuole,* which is a storage place for food, sugar, minerals, water, and other materials. In some cells the vacuole is used to discharge waste matter.

A cell, being mostly liquid, is enclosed and held in shape by a thin transparent membrane (4), a sort of skin. Without this membrane the protoplasm would flow out. Within the cell are membranes around the nucleus and the vacuole. In each cell the protoplasm constructs these membranes.

A plant cell is similar to an animal cell, except that plant cells have outer membranes, or walls, which serve as a framework for the plant. Most cell walls are composed chiefly of the substance called *cellulose.* In some parts of the plant, as in tree trunks, the cell walls are quite thick. They are used by man as wood to build houses and to make furniture, and for the manufacture of paper and artificial fibers. This type of cell wall forms most of the fibers produced by plants, such as cotton, flax, and

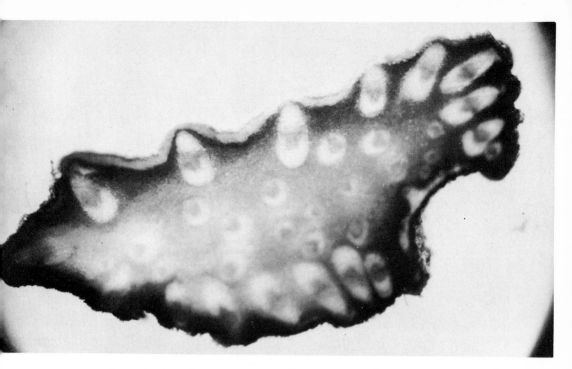

The red plastids in a portion of a geranium flower.

hemp. The plant cells with softer and thinner walls, such as those of leaves, stems, stalks, roots, flowers, fruits, and seeds, are used for food by many animals, including man.

Within the cytoplasm of the plant cell are colored disks or ribbons, called *plastids* (5). The green plastid in leaf cells contains *chlorophyll*, by means of which the plant manufactures its food. Yellow and red plastids give color to the flowers and fruits. A colorless plastid is a storage house for starch. In the photomicrograph of the alga cell on page 85 the equally spaced oval objects (6) in the green plastids are food reserves, mostly grains of starch.

In many-celled plants and animals there is a division of work between cells. Tree cells are specialized; various cells in the trunk serve as traffic lanes for the transport of food, others in the leaves manufacture the food, and still others anchor the tree in the soil and support its branches. The cells in man are

87

Milkweed seeds, emerging from their pods, each with a tuft of slender hairs for dispersal by wind. Cells of one hair are shown at right.

specialized; some are the eyes, others are bone, skin, brain, and so on. All the cells of the individual organism are dependent upon one another. To be alive means cooperation by every cell for the life and the welfare of the entire body of cells.

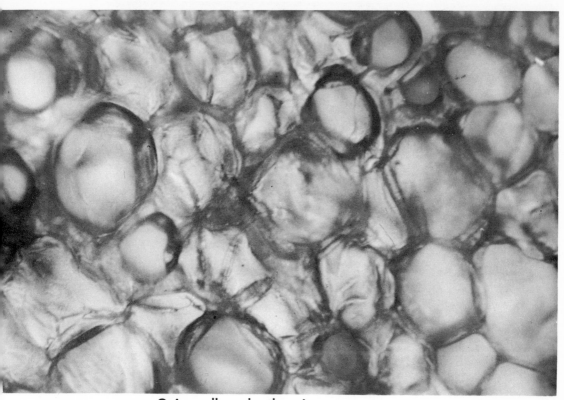

Onion cells under the microscope.

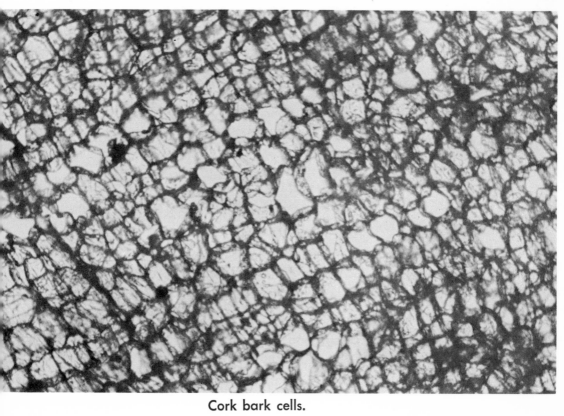

Cork bark cells.

Each sunflower
seed has a distinc-
tive color pattern.
Below: The stripes
are caused by the
arrangement of
elongated cells
which contain
plastids.

For a general study of plant cells under the microscope, the
algae are very satisfactory. Since most algae are transparent and
thin, their cell structure is plainly visible.

The Algae

Have you noticed a bright green scum floating on the surface of a lake or pond near the shore? This green matter consists of members of a large group called *algae*. There are eighteen thousand varieties of algae, ranging in size from minute organisms to giant forms, and all are interesting.

Some large algae can be found at the seashore. Seaweed is an alga. The green slime on the rocks along the beach is composed of algae, and this most widely distributed plant grows also in the deeper waters of all oceans.

Algae belong to the group of simplest plants, the *thallophytes*, which is from the Greek name for a young shoot plant. This group is divided into three branches: bacteria, fungi, and algae. The algae differ from the fungi and bacteria by having the green coloring matter, chlorophyll, which is found in the higher plants. Fungi and bacteria do not have chlorophyll.

Algae are divided into five major groups. The first group is known as the blue-green algae, as they contain both blue and green plastids. These plants can be found on the waters of warm ponds, on damp rocks and wet tree trunks, in polluted water, and even in hot springs. Many of these plants are slimy to the touch.

The second group is the green algae, which contains only green plastids. They live mostly in fresh water.

The third group is the brown algae. To this group belongs the seaweed. The color of the brown algae varies from brown to olive green, depending on the amount of brown pigment

Thousands of cells of a green alga which grows on the surface of fresh-water ponds.

A brown alga, which grows in shallow ocean waters attached to rocks.

The delicate branches of a marine red alga.

mixed with the green. Brown algae are found mostly in the shallow waters of the seas in cool regions. In the Arctic Ocean some of them grow to be a hundred feet long.

The fourth group, the red algae, is found mainly in warmer seas, growing in deep waters as much as two hundred feet below the surface of the ocean. Their colors range from bright red to purple, depending on the red plastids in the cell. Most red algae are delicate, feathery plants with many branches.

The fifth group, called the *diatoms,* lives in both fresh and salt water. Diatoms are minute algae which serve as a food source for fish and other aquatic animals. They are unique because each cell is like a little pillbox. The top and bottom cell wall is made of silica, the mineral used in the production of glass. When the diatom dies, the mineral part of the cell, or the skeleton, settles to the bottom of the ocean. Many ages ago, billions of skeletons formed huge beds of so-called diatomaceous earth. Millions of years later, wherever the ocean receded to expose these deposits, the diatomaceous earth became useful to man. It is used as a filter in the production of sugar and gasoline, for insulator wrappings around steam pipes, for soundproofing, and as a fine polishing powder. Each one of these tiny transparent skeletons in diatomaceous earth is a jewel of amazing beauty.

An alga cell functions as a complete plant. It grows, multiplies, and feeds itself. It produces its food as the higher forms of plants do, from water and dissolved minerals, from the gases in the water and in the air, with the chemical action of its chlorophyll and the energy of sunlight.

Try this interesting experiment to test the presence of starch in algae. Place one group of algae in a dark, moist box for a number of hours and keep another group in daylight. Test each

95

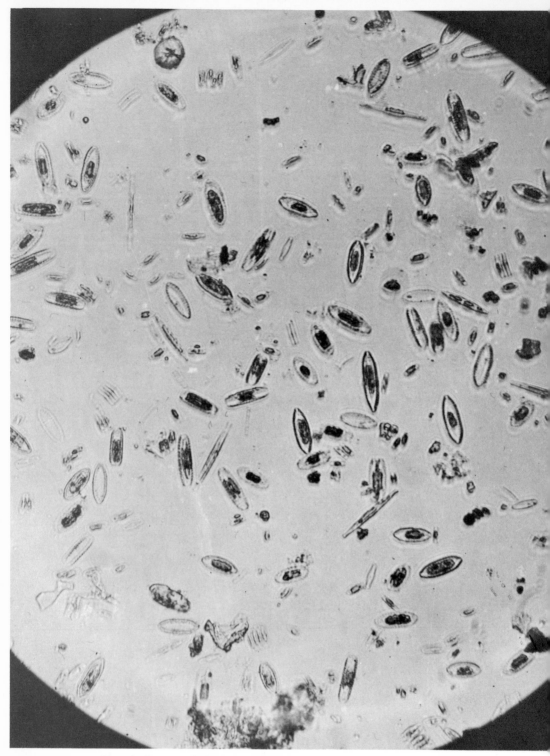

The skeletons of diatoms, a group of algae, have diverse shapes.

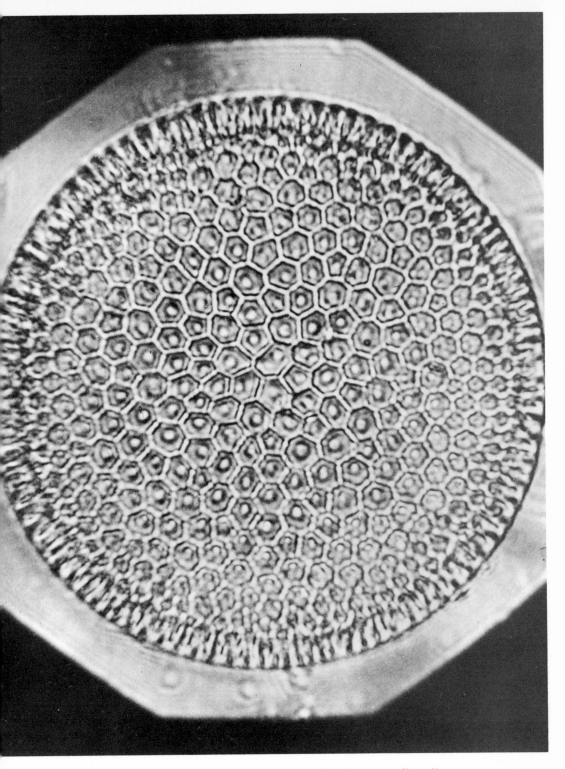

The microscope reveals the lovely design of a diatom cell wall.

group by adding to it a small drop of a weak solution of iodine, which will turn starch blue. The group which has been kept in the dark either will not stain blue or will become a very light blue, because all or most of its starch has been made into sugar which the plant needed as food. Now make the iodine test on the algae that was in the daylight; it will turn blue. Apply this test to leaves of higher plants and notice the reaction similar to that of the algae.

Algae multiply in three different ways. In some algae the cell, when fully grown, splits in two across the center to form two new cells. These will also split when they have reached full growth. In this manner the chain of alga cells grows longer. In certain other algae two cells connect with each other and form a third. This cell, which is called a spore, starts a new growth of alga. In other species two large cells divide within themselves into a number of small ones which burst from the larger, older cells to combine with one another and form new alga plants.

At the end of summer, old fresh-water plants die. The young cells sink below the surface of lakes and rivers and remain there throughout the winter. In spring the young alga cells rise up to the surface of the water to grow anew.

Gather some pond scum and examine it. Most likely you will find that it consists of fine and slippery threads, characteristic of the most common kind of pond scum, the algae called *Spirogyra*. Under your microscope you will notice that it has a number of shapes. Each thread is a chain of alga cells. One of these chains has what appears to be a spiral coiled around it, like the one shown in the illustration. This alga is a filament of single-celled plants, every cell connecting with another to form a chain. Each cell is clearly marked off from the rest by a line on each

Spirogyra, a fresh-water algae.

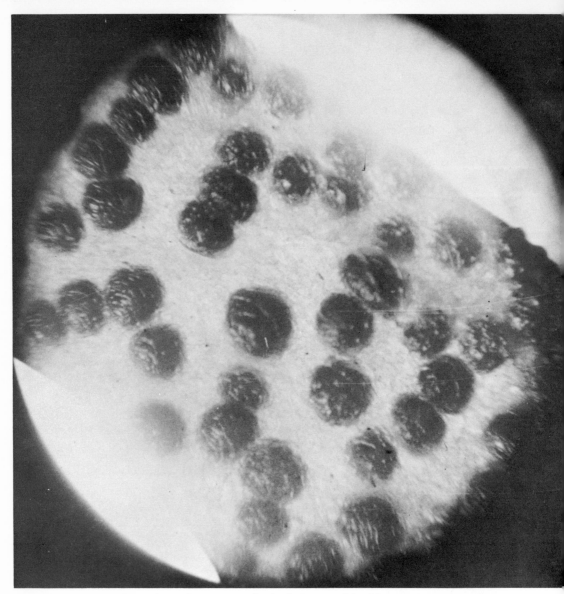

A section of a seaweed which has air bladders to keep it afloat.

end of the cell. If the chain should be broken, each cell can live by itself and start a new chain.

Scrape off some of the green stain which you see on a moist tree trunk or a rock. Clean it with water and examine it under the microscope. The alga cells are round and bright green when wet. You will see some which stick together in large masses, others which form groups of four, and some that are single.

The brown algae, to which the seaweed belongs, are fastened to rocks below the water's surface by rootlike structures. Unlike the roots of higher plants, these structures provide no nourishment to the plant, but they help it to withstand the buffeting of the tides.

Seaweed keeps afloat by means of air-filled bladders which are distributed over the body of the plant. It grows by branching at its ends. Some brown algae become huge, with treelike branches many feet long. After a storm many brown algae can be found floating in the surf and cast up on the shore.

Algae are of utmost importance to all life. Not only are they the basic food source for fish and other aquatic animals, but some algae are used by man as food. Other species are used in the manufacture of ice cream, gelatin, candy, toothpaste, and drugs.

The microscopic study of this large division of plant life can keep anyone busy through an entire summer at the seashore or in the country.

A fungus growing on dead and decaying vegetation of the forest floor.

The Fungi

Green plants make their own food, but fungi, having no chlorophyll, are unable to do this and must use ready-made food. Some fungi feed upon dead plant or animal matter and others obtain their food as parasites from the tissues of living organisms.

Fungi which depend on decaying matter for food are beneficial because they dispose of the dead and waste products of nature. Parasitic fungi are harmful because they destroy thousands of trees and many bushels of food crops annually, and some infect humans and domestic animals. Millions of dollars are spent every year for research to discover effective chemicals for the control of harmful fungi.

Cut a raw potato in half and keep it warm and moist in the shade. A day or so later examine the cut surfaces carefully. A white threadlike substance which is a fungus has begun to grow on the potato. Cut off very thin sections of the surface daily and study the development of the fungus under the microscope. After some time small branches, or stalks, will rise from the

Fungus growth on a slice of raw potato.

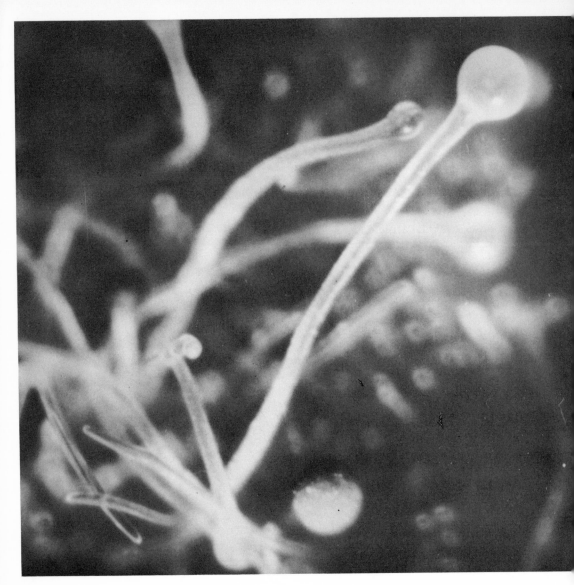

Fungus growth on a prune pit. The stalks with the spore-bearing capsules are fully grown.

potato. Examine the tips of the stalks. They contain the seeds of the fungus, which are called spores. The stalk tips eventually open and eject the spores.

Fungus spores are always floating in the air. When one drops upon the surface of a moist potato in a warm place, the conditions for its growth are very favorable. A fungus plant will develop, and in a short time it produces new spores.

The fungus threads, which penetrate the surface tissues in all directions, provide the food for growth. Solid material, such as bread, has to be changed by these threads before it can be used for their nourishment. The fungus does this by discharging a chemical into the bread, which its threads can then absorb.

Many species of fungi which are parasites on living organisms also have this means of dissolving their food. When a tree has an open wound caused by a broken branch or by an animal rubbing off a strip of bark, a fungus may begin to grow in that spot. The threads of the fungus can enter the tree and dissolve the living cells until the entire tree is destroyed.

Parasitic fungi called smuts, rusts, mildews, and blights attack cultivated plants, such as fruit trees, potato, corn, wheat, and rye. Millions of fruit trees and other food crops have been destroyed by these fungi. After the entire potato crop of Ireland was destroyed by potato-blight fungus in 1845-1846, thousands of people died of starvation and hundreds of thousands fled to America to avoid hunger.

There are other types of fungi, called blue and green molds, which can be grown very easily. Mix some fruit gelatin with water and let it harden. In two or three days a small fungus plant will appear on the surface. Study it carefully and notice how it grows outward from a central point. After several days this fungus will become green.

The blue molds on bread, cheese, and other substances belong to a genus called *Penicillium*. One of these species produces penicillin, a substance beneficial in fighting some diseases of man. It kills or inactivates many types of the bacteria which cause various diseases in human beings.

Another important and beneficial fungus is *yeast*. Like the spores of other fungi, those of yeast float about in the air. Plants developing from airborne spores are called wild yeast to distinguish them from the cultivated yeast used in alcoholic fermentation and in the manufacture of bread.

If your microscope is capable of magnifying about two hundred and fifty times, here is an interesting experiment. Make a solution composed of one part sugar to ten parts of lukewarm water. Into this solution put a pinch of dry yeast, and keep it uncovered in a warm place. Bubbles will soon rise. These bubbles consist of alcohol and the gas called carbon dioxide. The next day place a very small drop of this liquid in a cavity slide under a microscope. A great number of small oval and colorless cells will be floating in the liquid. These are yeast cells. When a cell has grown to its full size, a small cell will start growing at one end, and after some time this small cell will split off from the parent cell. This process is called budding; by it a yeast cell, when placed in a favorable solution, will grow and multiply rapidly.

For bread dough the cultivated yeast is mixed with starch, sugar, and warm water. As the yeast develops, the bubbles of carbon dioxide and alcohol expand the dough and make it rise. When the bread is baked, the alcohol and the carbon dioxide have been driven off by the heat, but the bread remains porous and light as a result of the expansion and thus is fit for eating.

When a fruit is crushed, the wild yeast spores clinging to the moist skin become active and penetrate the bruised surface of the fruit. Alcohol and carbon dioxide bubble up from the crushed

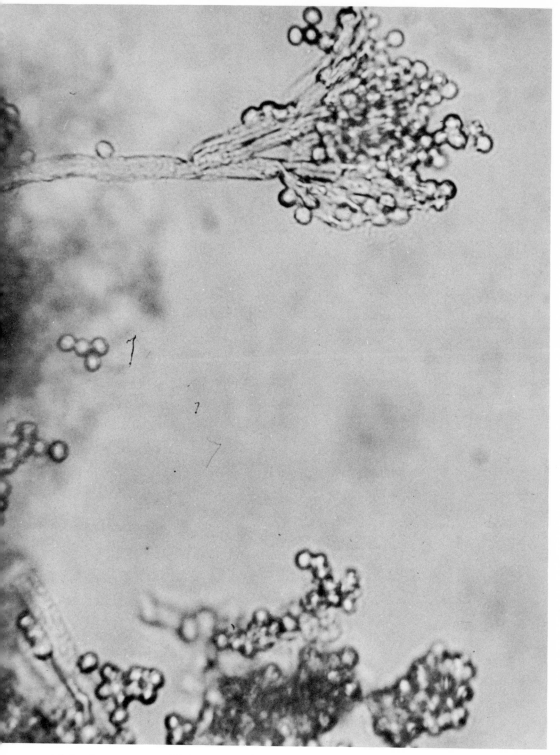

A blue fungus, or mold, found on cheese and lemons. A closely related fungus produces the antibiotic penicillin.

A group of wild mushrooms.

fruit. The chemical change brought about by the yeast is known as fermentation. This process is essential in brewing beer and in making wine and industrial alcohol.

The mushroom is a fungus. Some species are used as food. The cultivated mushroom which we eat is not the entire plant, but the stalk and cap, similar to the spore-bearing stalks which you saw growing upward on a raw potato. The threadlike structures of mushroom plants remain in the ground for years. Examine the stalk of the mushroom and notice that it is made up of many fine threads. The stalk expands on the top into an umbrella-shaped form, the cap. Underneath this cap there are layers of small thin sections called gills, which contain the spores of the mushroom. When the spores are ripe, they drop to the ground or are blown away by the wind to start new plants.

Cut out one of the thin layers under the cap and press it between two slides. Under the microscope you will see the minute spores.

Here is an experiment. Break off the caps of two mushrooms from their stalks. Lay one on a white sheet of paper and cover it with a bowl. Lay the other on a black sheet of paper and cover it. The next day uncover them and gently pick up the caps. Underneath, on the papers, you will see the spores arranged in a pattern just as they have fallen out of the gills. This is called a spore print. The spores may have different colors, which are easier to see against either a white or a black background.

Some species called bracket fungi commonly grow on dead and decaying trees, the threads of these fungi penetrating the dead wood on which they feed. Bracket fungi are sometimes parasites upon living trees.

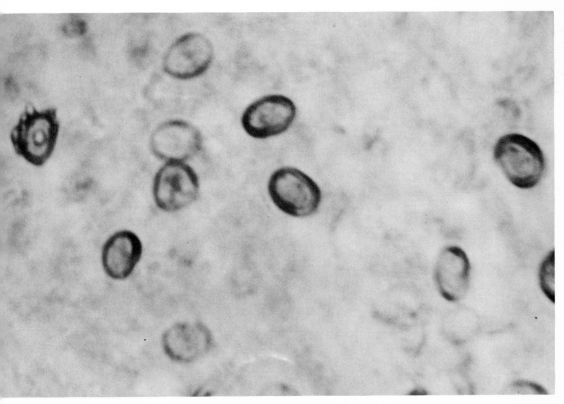

Spores of a mushroom.

Bracket fungi on a dead tree.

On the bark of trees, on fences or stones, you may find a grayish-green substance which is a plant called lichen. It is found in three main forms—a powdery crust, a low-growing plant with leaflike structures, or an erect or hanging plant with numerous slender branches. Scrape off a small bit of a lichen and examine it under the microscope. You will see many green cells entwined in white threads. The lichen is composed really of two plants, a green alga and a colorless fungus; hence the grayish-green color. The alga has been captured by the fungus, but they live together harmoniously. The alga provides food for the fungus, and the fungus provides the alga with water and support.

A group of moss plants.

The Mosses

Wherever one goes, in woods or fields, high up in the mountains or in the warm, shady wet spots and swamps of the lowlands, one is sure to find moss. It is one of the most widely distributed plants on earth. But not all small plants growing close to the ground and on rocks are mosses. They may be algae or lichens or even small flowering plants.

The moss plant has not changed for millions of years. It is more closely related to the green algae than to the complex flowering plants, as it has no specialized cells for supporting it in the soil, nor special cells for conducting water and minerals and for storing food. Each leaflike stem of the moss draws water and minerals from the soil by means of small rootlike extensions.

Moss grows on moist soil, on tree trunks, and on rocks. It flourishes in very shady places and in all climates, including the arctic zones. It is especially prolific in the cool, moist forests of the northwestern United States.

Moss acts like a carpet on the soil, holding water long after the rains have stopped. Thus it protects the soil from drying out and prevents erosion. Seeds from many plants falling on moss-covered soil find it a good place to grow and thrive. In this manner moss helps to increase the number of trees in the forest.

Collect moss with a strip of soil attached. Mount the strip lengthwise on a slide. Looking at it through the microscope you cannot fail to see the beauty of the moss.

The scaly leaflike moss is only one cell thick. Place a section in a drop of water and examine it under the microscope. At the tip you may see club-shaped extensions, some of which contain the egg cells, and from these come the spores which develop into new moss plants.

Take a single plant from a group of mosses, plant it, and keep it moist. Watch it grow, germinate, and increase.

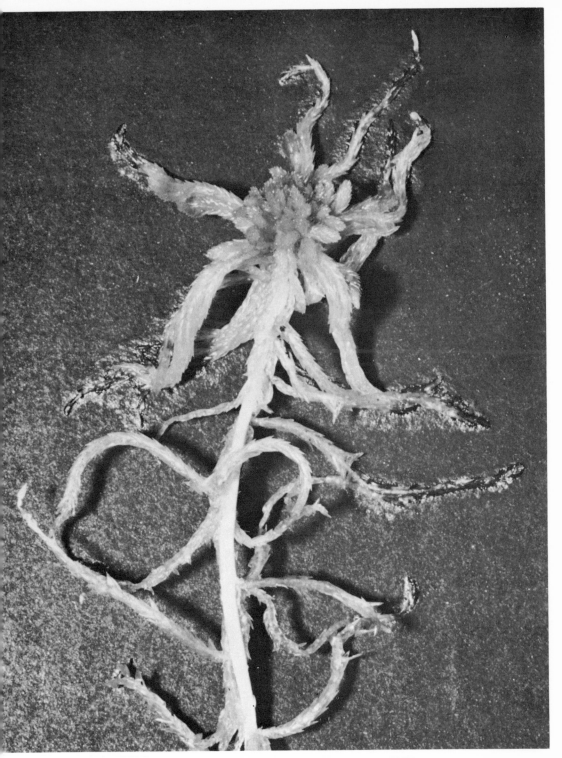

A peat-moss plant is only about a half inch in height.

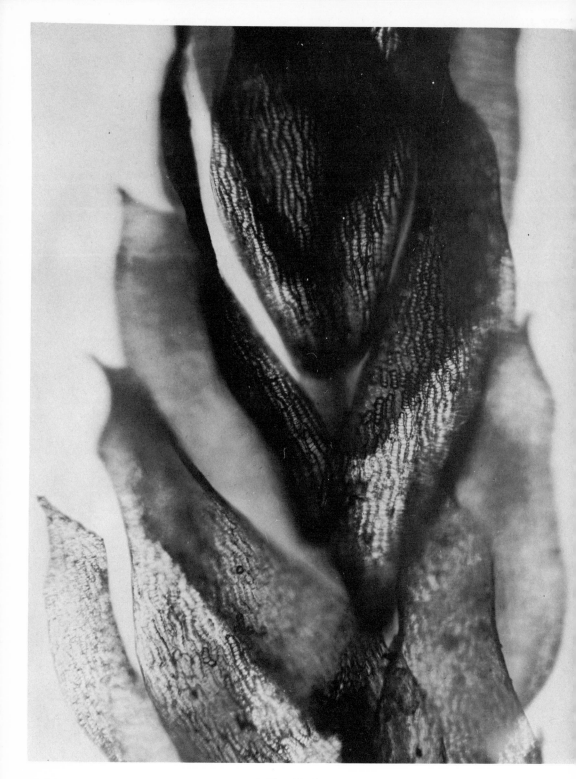

A "leaf" of peat moss.

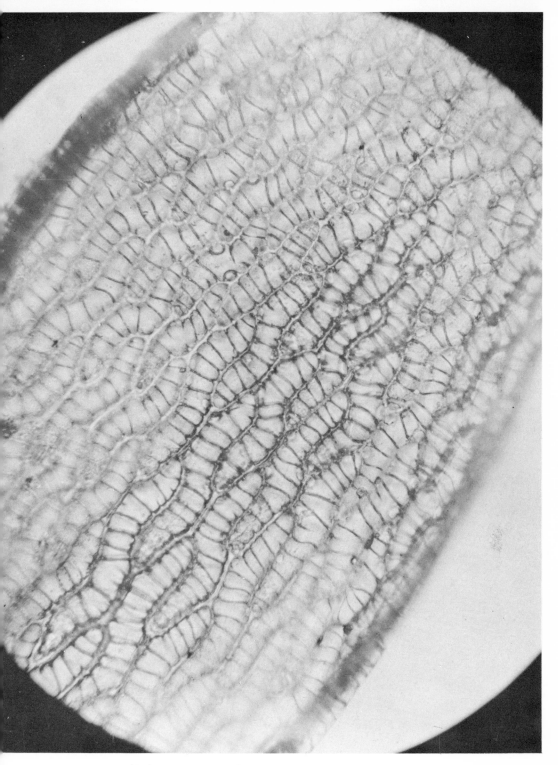

A section of the peat-moss "leaf," showing its cell structure.

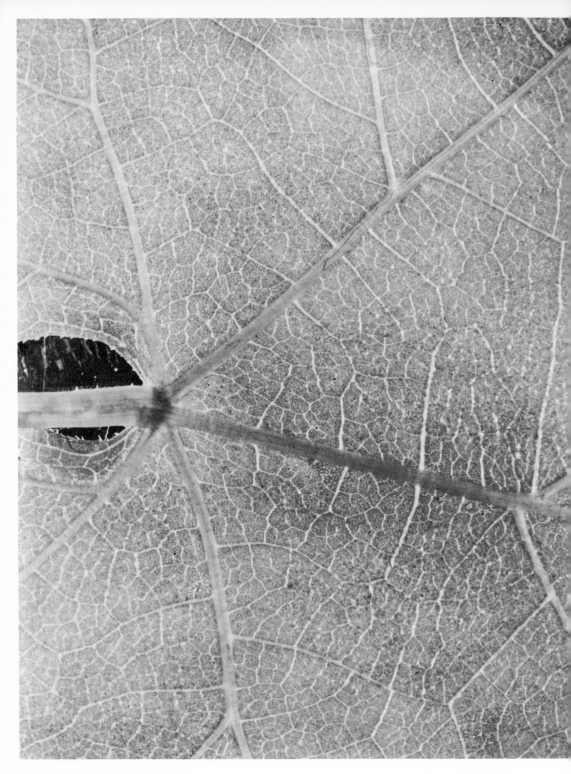

The underside of a leaf reveals the network of veins branching out from the stem and interconnecting the entire surface. Through this network the leaf receives water and minerals from the roots and sends food to other parts of the plant.

The Leaf

The leaf is the food factory of the higher plant. Gases from the air enter through the pores of the leaf, and water and minerals absorbed from the soil by the root are brought to the leaf through the stem. By the chemical action of chlorophyll in the leaf cells and the energy of light, raw materials from the air and soil are combined to make the food of the plant.

Man and all animals are completely dependent for life upon plants. Grains, vegetables, fruits, meat and fish—all our food sources—come directly or indirectly from plants. Without the ability of leaves to make food for plants, all life on earth would be impossible.

The leaf makes sugar which the entire plant uses as food. During daylight it makes more sugar than is necessary for immediate use. Some of it is changed into cellulose, the building material of the plant, and much of it is changed into other food compounds, including starch, which is stored up in various parts of the plant. At night, when no sugar is made, the starch is changed back into sugar for use by the plant.

In the production of its food, the leaf releases oxygen into the air. Every year all over the world thousands of billions of leaves are growing, making their food, and releasing enormous quantities of oxygen into the atmosphere. That is why the air in the forest is so fresh and pure. Some scientists believe that much of the present-day oxygen in the atmosphere was produced by plants that have grown on this planet through millions of years.

The plant sends more water to the leaf than it needs to manufacture food. A great amount of water evaporates from the broad surfaces of the leaf, especially during hot summer days, thus cooling the leaf and keeping it from shriveling. If the plant cannot supply all the water needed, the leaf dies. Many plant leaves have fine hairs growing close to their surface to prevent water from evaporating too rapidly. Others protect their water supply by pointing the broad part of the leaf surface north and south so that only the weaker rays of the morning and afternoon sun will reach them. This is true of plants which live in open fields where there is intense sunlight. The leaves of plants living in shady places turn their surfaces to the point from which the most direct sunlight comes. The leaves of some plants fold, curl up, or droop at night, but at sunrise they resume their daytime positions.

Leaves of many plants are short-lived in the temperate zone. Cherry, peach, oak, and maple leaves can be seen from spring through fall. The leaves of fir, spruce, and pine are long-lived, remaining attached to the plant for two or more years. Such plants are called evergreens. One can find green leaves all the year round in the tropics.

We use the leaves of spinach, lettuce, and celery for food, tobacco leaves for smoking, and tea leaves for making tea. For flavoring and in medicine a few of the many leaves used are witch hazel, arnica, horehound, and spearmint. Leaves of many plants, especially those of the grasses, are used as food by grazing animals, such as cows, sheep, and horses.

Examine the leaves of many plants—grasses, bushes, and trees—and notice how they vary in structure. Some are thick, broad, or narrow. Under the microscope observe the hairs on

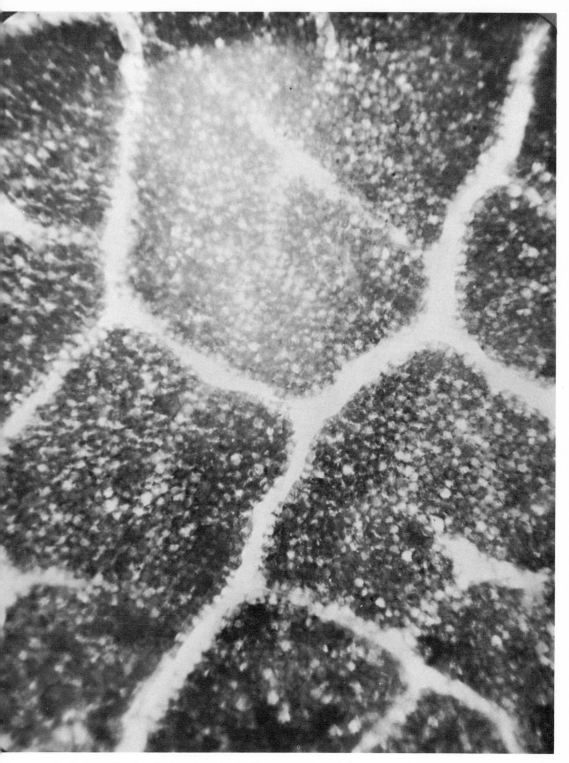

A section of a leaf, showing the cell structure and the veins which serve as highways for the plant.

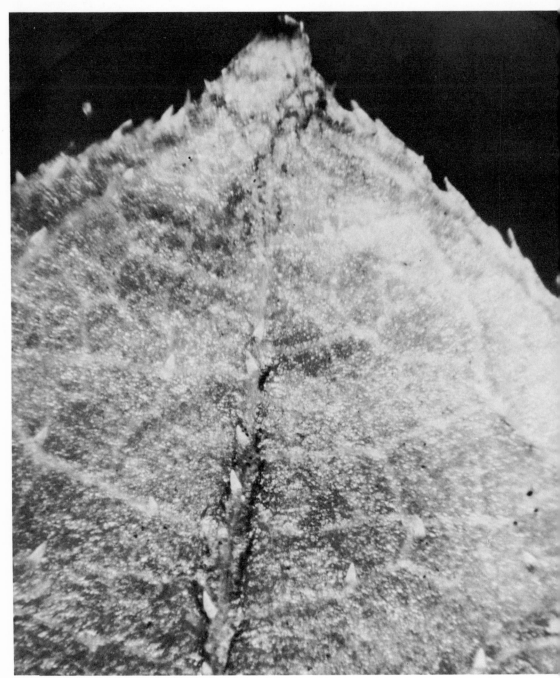

The small, white triangular shapes are "hairs" on the surface of a leaf.

the leaves. Some are soft and silky; others are stiff like spines. Notice that the leaves from various plants have different shapes. Each plant species has a specifically shaped leaf. It is interesting to grow a lima bean in a small flower pot and watch the development of its leaves.

The base of a tree with its upper root system, which radiates outward to anchor the tree in the soil.

The Root

In seed plants the part of the plant which is in the soil is called the root. Unearth a bundle of grass very carefully and wash it. You will see the main part of the root continuing downward from the stem of the grass. It divides into many branches. The

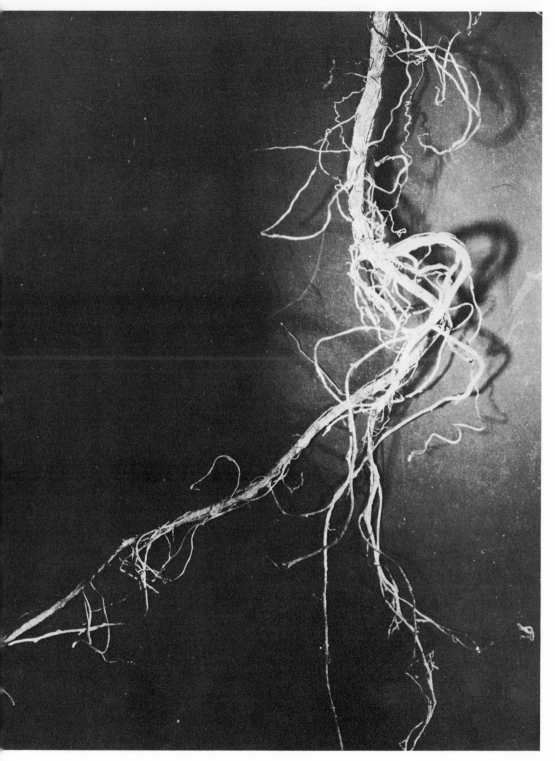

From the main root in the upper part of the picture grow branch roots, and from these grow fine extensions called the root hairs.

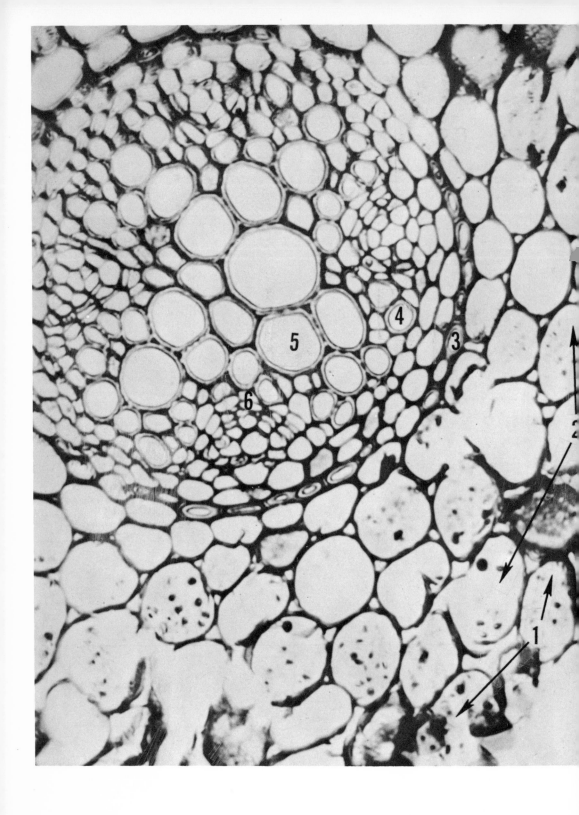

main root grows downward into the soil and the branched roots grow sideways. In this manner all parts of the soil beneath the plant are firmly gripped.

On the lower part of the root, near the tip, are thin outgrowths called root hairs. These delicate filaments spread into the surrounding soil, making it possible for the plant to absorb very large amounts of water.

Roots of plants penetrate from four to fifteen feet into the soil. Even the roots of large trees do not go deeper. They spread out sideways, however, over large areas to absorb the minerals and water in the earth.

Cut a very thin cross-section from a root. At the rim is a single layer of cells (1), the outside skin of the root. These cells and the root hairs which grow out of them absorb large amounts of water which is transported to the next inner layer of cells (2). Here water, minerals, and food are stored. Beyond these is a ring of cells (3) only one cell wide. These form a kind of inside skin surrounding a center of various kinds of cells. The large and thick-walled cells (4 and 5) transport water and minerals, and the thin-walled smaller cells (6) conduct the food made by the leaves to other parts of the plant. Between these are clusters of special growth cells which extend the root into the soil.

In general this cell arrangement is the same in the trunk and the woody stems of plants, except that the outer layer, called bark, is formed of hard dead cells.

Put a lima bean on a blotter with just enough water to keep it moist, or place a cutting of geranium, ivy, or philodendron in a glass jar filled with water, and watch the root develop.

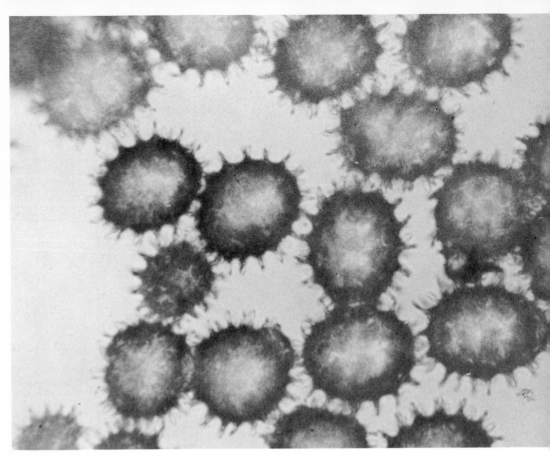

Pollen of the sunflower appears as a yellow, shapeless powder until it is seen through the microscope.

Pollen and Seeds

Higher plants reproduce by means of pollen and seeds, and must distribute them widely in order to survive and multiply.

Pollen is a powdery, yellow, generally sticky substance consisting of many small grains no larger than 1/700th to 1/300th of an inch thick. The shape of a pollen grain may be round, oval, or cylindrical, and its outside surface may have spines, ridges, tiny

126

A pine cone which bears ovules. At upper left is a grain of pine pollen, which has little "wings" that carry it through the air. Some of the grains fall on the ovules of pine cones.

The fragrant, orange-colored flowers of the butterfly weed are typical of those that attract the bees and butterflies which disseminate the pollen.

wings, or other markings, depending on the plant from which it comes. In flowering plants the pollen is borne in the flowers; in pine and other conifers it is borne in small cones.

Inside each grain are the cells which help make a new plant. When a pollen grain comes in contact with the ovule—another structure in the plant, which bears the egg cell—the cells inside the grain burst through the grain walls and unite with the cell

128

inside the ovule. From this union is formed the seed of the new plant. This process is called pollination.

A common method of pollen distribution is by the cooperation of plants and insects. Many plants grow colorful flowers which have a pleasant perfume and a sweet-tasting liquid called nectar. The color or odor of the flower attracts flying insects, such as the bee and the butterfly. The flowers are so constructed that these insects can easily reach the pollen and become powdered with it. Hence, while the honeybee gathers pollen and nectar for food, it carries pollen on its body and distributes some of it.

Watch a bee on a flower. When it flies away it will be covered with pollen. In gathering pollen, the bee visits many flowers of the same kind. Some of the pollen of the first flower which is on the legs of the bee will be brushed off on the ovule of the second flower. In this way pollination between two flowers of the same kind takes place.

Air currents are another method of pollen distribution. Pollen which is carried by the wind is very powdery and light; the plant releases it into the air and some of the numerous grains fall on similar plants.

The seeds and fruits of plants are also ingeniously distributed. The seed of some trees, such as maple and pine, is carried by small wings which float it gracefully through the air. Other plants, such as the thistle, dandelion, and milkweed, have small tufts of hair attached to each seed. When the seeds become ripe, the wind takes them from the plant and they float away like small white parachutes or balloons. In this manner the plant distributes itself rapidly over the countryside.

When the fruits of certain plants, such as a fern, witch hazel, and wild bean, become ripe, they burst open and eject their

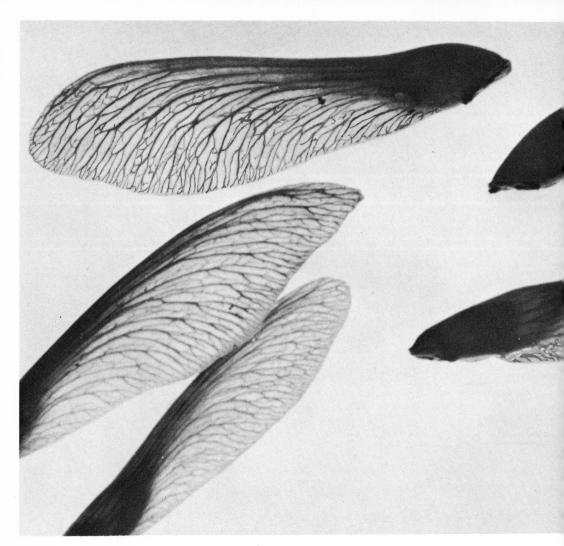

Maple-tree seeds. The wind whirls them about until they land, sometimes at quite a distance from the parent tree.

seeds over the ground. Another means of seed dispersal is by the barbs, spines, and hairs that grow on the surface of the fruits of certain plants. When an animal brushes past the plant, these fruits stick to the animal's fur and may be carried many miles before falling off. Burrs and "stickers" are typical of such fruits.

Many plants enclose their seeds with a fleshy and generally round or oval fruit. Some plants have brightly colored fruits that

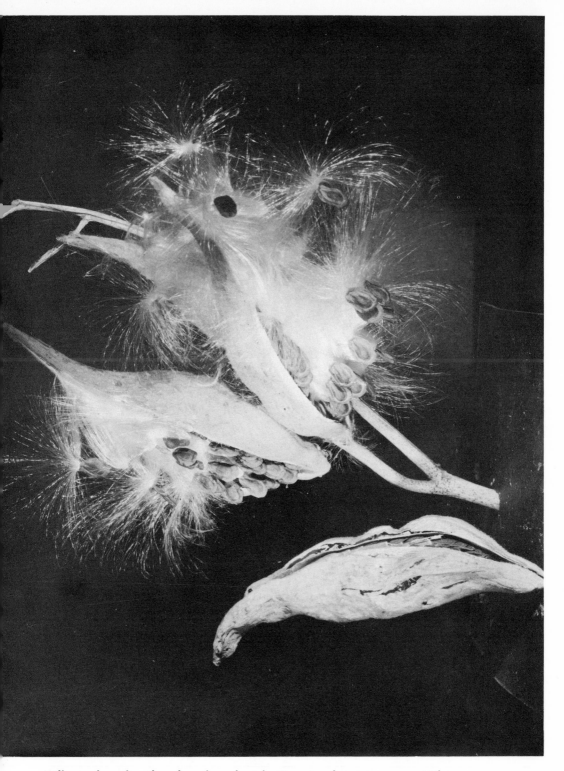

Milkweed pods. The closed pod at bottom is about to open. When open, the pods release their seeds to the wind. Attached to each seed is a tuft of fine white hairs which will float it through the air.

The white fruit of the bayberry is not too big to be swallowed whole by a small bird.

Sunflower seeds.

are attractive to birds. When the bird eats these fruits, the seeds pass unharmed through its stomach. The seeds of grapes, bayberries, cherries, and many other plants are distributed in this way.

The seeds of plants which grow on the shores of streams and lakes drop into the water, which distributes them. These seeds are well protected and can float for several weeks until they are cast up on the banks.

133

A dandelion seed with its plume of hair may be carried for miles by the wind.

An interesting experiment that illustrates seed dispersal by water is to gather some mud from the shallow bottom near the shores of a pond in the autumn and spread it about two inches thick in a little pan. Many kinds of plants will grow from the seeds in this soil.

Gather different flowers, carefully remove the pollen grains, and study them under the microscope. Make a collection of seeds. Observe their appearance and shapes. Soak the seeds in water until they are soft; then you can easily cut them and

Grass seeds.

Burdock has its seeds encased in a barbed capsule. The tiny hooks catch on the hair of passing animals and thus help to disperse the seeds.

The plant called false Solomon's seal bears its seeds in bright-red berries, an attractive food for birds.

observe their cell arrangements under the microscope. Plant a grapefruit seed in a little earth in a glass jar. Put the seed close to the wall of the jar so that you can observe it as it begins to grow.

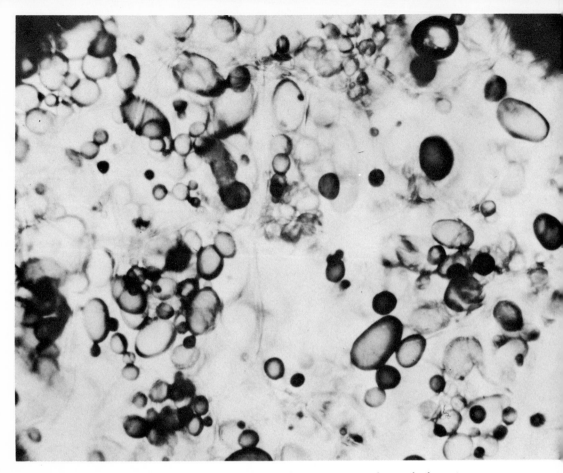

Starch cells in a little scraping of potato, seen through the microscope. The starch cells have been darkened by the application of a weak solution of iodine.

Starch

We get our energy for work and play from plants in the form of starch, which is a compound substance of carbon, hydrogen, and oxygen. In the plant sugar becomes converted into starch and is stored for future use in different parts of the plant body.

In the cytoplasm of the plant cell, a colorless plastid is the storage chamber for starch. This plastid is a thin membrane

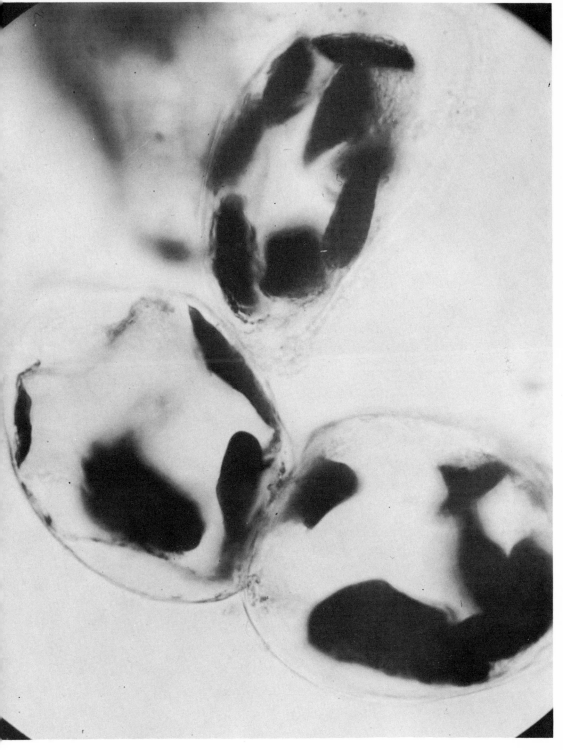

The black spots are starch grains in banana cells.

enclosing one or more starch grains. Since each plant species has a differently shaped starch grain, it is possible to identify a plant by inspecting its starch grains under the microscope. Potato starch is shaped somewhat like oyster shells, wheat starch is round, and cornstarch may be round or angular, depending upon the part of the kernel from which it comes.

Put in separate test tubes a pinch of cornstarch, flour, banana, rice, apple, and a section of a plant stem, and add a little water in each tube. Shake up the water and material, and let each tube stand until the water is almost clear and most of the material has settled to the bottom. Examine a drop of each solution and of each sediment. Observe that the shape and size of the starch grains are different in each tube. Test the starch with a weak solution of iodine.

Wheat grains, from which we make flour and then bread, are seventy-five-per-cent starch. Potatoes, rice, and many other plants have a high starch content.

In plants the starch is converted back into sugar when it is needed for food. Let us find out what happens to the starch we eat. Place in a test tube a small amount of cornstarch mixed with a large amount of your own saliva. As you examine a drop of this solution under the microscope, you will see the starch cells begin to change. Test the drop with iodine; it will turn blue. About every five minutes examine a drop of the solution and make the iodine test. At one point the iodine will turn red instead of blue, indicating that the starch grains are being digested by the saliva. Eventually the solution will not react to the iodine test. Examination under the microscope will confirm the absence of starch grains. The saliva has turned all the starch into sugar.

Hair, Feathers, and Scales

Most plants and animals, including insects, have outgrowths from the outermost layer of cells. These are called hairs, scales, or feathers. Hair is so commonly seen in nature that we often are not aware of it.

Animal hair protects against cold weather by trapping air warmed by the body between its strands. Its coloration in an animal or insect may blend into the landscape, thus protecting the creature from its enemies.

The structure of human hair is interesting. That part below the skin is the root, which is bulb-shaped. From the root upward and above the skin grows the shaft, which is made up of three sections. The inner section is called the medulla, the next section is the cortex, and the outer section is a very thin layer of cells called the cuticle. Between the cells which make up the cortex of the hair is the pigment that gives it color. Gray hair is caused by the absence of pigment.

When we are very angry or become frightened, our hair "stands up on end" or we get "gooseflesh." This is caused by a small muscle attached to the base of each hair which contracts and so pulls the hair up. The frightened cat with its "bushy" tail is a good example of what these muscles can do.

When a hair falls out, it usually breaks at the root, leaving the root in the skin. The root becomes active and a new shaft grows. When the roots fall out with the hair, the result is permanent baldness. The life of each hair growing on the head is about four years, but an eyebrow hair lasts only about four to five months.

A human hair with its root.

Hair is not equally distributed over the entire body but grows thickly only in the places where it serves the best purpose. We have thicker hair on our heads than anywhere else on our body probably because many thousands of years ago, long before hats were used, primitive man needed a covering against the rain and cold for the top of his head.

The mane of the horse, which is very thick in the wild animal, is a protection for its neck because it is the most weakly defended part of its body. The hairs growing at the end of the tails of horses and cows are used for swishing away flies. The long hairy tail of the squirrel helps to balance it in leaping from tree to tree, and when the squirrel wraps its tail around its body the hairs serve as a protection from the cold and as a disguise against the prying eyes of its enemies.

The hairs on each side of a cat's mouth and above the eyes extend outward as far as or farther than the width of its body. With these sensitive hairs, or feelers, the cat is able to judge whether a hole is large enough for it to go through.

Many animals shed their hair before the approach of winter and grow a new and thicker coat for better protection against cold and rain and snow. Animals that live in the far north, such as the fox and the ermine, acquire a white coat in winter. This color transformation is a protection against enemies, because the region in which they live alters from the green and brown of summer to the brilliant white of winter.

The quality and thickness of hair differ greatly among animals. Porcupines have coarse, stiff hairs which we call spines. The soft hair of sheep is wool, and the fine, thick hair of wild animals is fur.

Bird feathers are another type of hair. They have two impor-

A magnified section of a bird feather. The small interlocking branches grow out of the main shafts.

tant uses—for flying and for bodily warmth. The wings are covered with feathers in a wonderfully efficient way. Wing feathers are very light and are arranged to resist the wind on the downstroke of the wing and to separate slightly on the upstroke, so that the air will pass through when wind resistance is a hindrance.

The principal part of a feather is the shaft which grows outward from the skin of the bird. On each side of that shaft grow smaller ones which have small branches that extend diagonally and interlock with the branches of the adjoining shafts. In this way the feather of a bird not only is very light but presents a flexible, waterproof surface.

The color of feathers is caused either by pigments or by iridescence. An iridescent feather changes its color because of the way in which its closely ribbed surface reflects the light. Similarly certain glassware shows color changes when turned about in different directions.

At the end of the breeding season, just before winter, many birds lose their bright feathers. This process is called molting. The new feathers in some species are colored so that they blend with the winter landscape and help to make the bird invisible to its enemies. These birds also molt in the spring, exchanging their dull winter feathers for a brightly colored coat.

The bird has other feathers distributed over its body. These are, for the most part, fine and downy, and serve the purpose of keeping its body warm.

Many insects have hairlike growths on their bodies. The scales on the wings and bodies of butterflies and moths are flattened-out hairs. Night-flying moths are thickly covered with scales to protect them against the cold. The short, stiff hairs on the wings of flies keep dirt particles from sticking to the wings. Longer

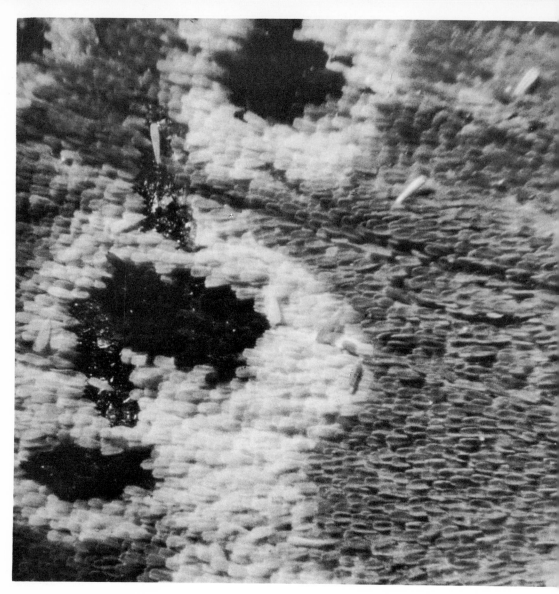

The wing of a moth. The flat hairs, or scales, overlap each other.

and thicker hairs grow near the joints of legs, overlapping and protecting that part of the insect's body. Around the sockets of the eyes of many insects there are protective hairs, as shown in the picture on page 148. On the feet of some insects, the hairs branch out on each side of the claw. These hairs are very thick

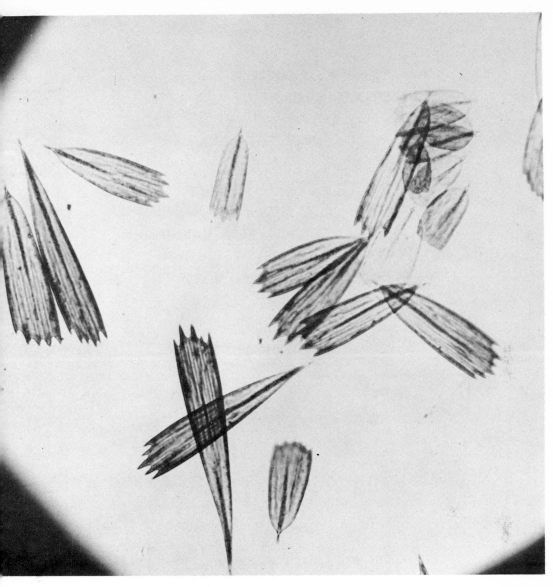

The scales of a moth's wing.

and stiff and are called bristles or spurs. They protect the claw from being damaged. Some insects that live on the surface of water have bunches of fine feathery hairs at the end of their feelers. By waving these feelers, the insect causes food particles in the water to flow into its mouth.

The hairs form a protective fringe around the compound eye of a fly.

The silver beetle that lives under water a good deal of the time has a growth of dense but very fine hairs on its sides. When the beetle comes to the surface, air bubbles stick to them. Under water the beetle sucks the air from these hairs and uses it for breathing. Many beetles which burrow into soil are thickly covered by strong hairs.

The larvae of many insects are hairy. The color of their hair not only makes them blend into their surroundings, but also protects them against their enemies.

Hair on the back of a beetle which lives in decaying trees.

The stems of a plant which have many hairy projections to ward off creeping insects.

Most plants have outgrowths which may be called hairs. Although their structure differs from that of hairs in animals, those of a plant furnish protection as do those of an animal. Insects are hindered from creeping up plant stems by such hairs.

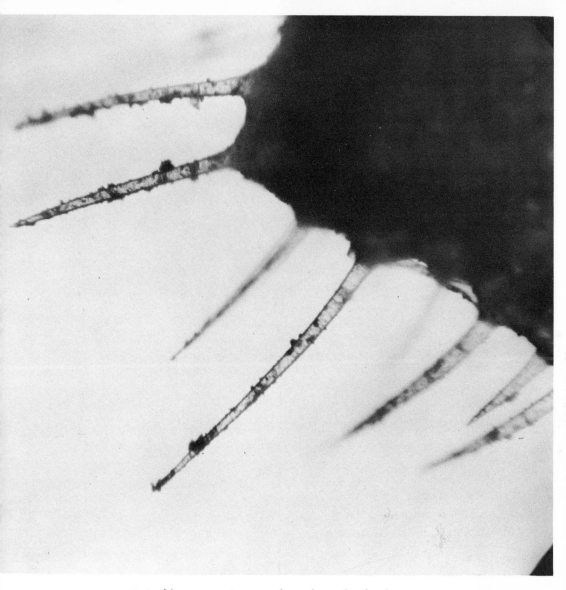

Spinelike projections at the edge of a leaf.

Some plants have thick, pointed spines on their stems that not only repulse insects but also prevent large animals from eating them. As we have seen, the fruits of many plants have hairs which cause them to cling to any passing animal, and in this

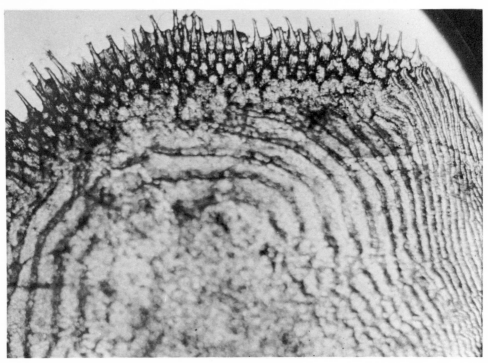

Fish scales.

manner the fruit is transported to other places where the seeds may have an opportunity to take root and grow. We have also seen that some seeds, such as the dandelion, have hairs to carry them through the air, and that the leaves of many plants have fine hairs all over their surfaces to prevent the rapid evaporation of water. (See pages 118 and 134.)

The scales covering the body of a fish consist of a strong, colorless mineral substance which protects the skin. Because scales are transparent, the color of the skin shows clearly through them. There are four kinds of scales, but we need mention only two, since the others are to be found on such fishes as the shark, with which you are not likely to come in contact. Only a few fishes such as the eel do not have scales.

Certain fishes have scales which are thick in the center and thin at the edges. The scales of others are round. Some scales have small projections, somewhat like the teeth of a comb, which hold them securely in the skin of the fish. Scales overlap one another like the shingles on a roof. The edge of the scale imbedded in the skin is overlapped by the outer portion of the adjoining scale.

The periods of the scale's growth are indicated by rings similar to those of a tree trunk. By means of these lines the age of the fish can be calculated.

Pull out a hair from your head very slowly, so that the root will come out with it. Examine it under the microscope and try to distinguish the various parts. Compare wool and fur. Notice the structure of a feather and compare a wing feather with a body feather. Under the microscope examine the hair of various caterpillars and insects. Compare the hairs on the wing of a butterfly with those on the wing of a fly. Notice how the hairs

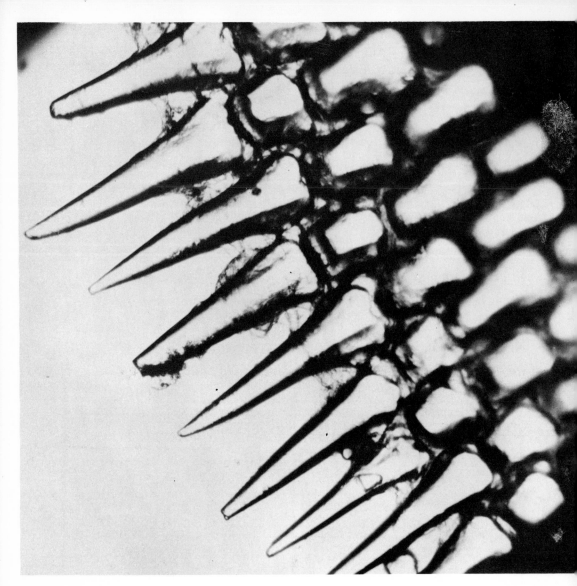

A fish scale is attached to the skin by spiny projections.

are attached. Compare them with the hairs on the body of any insect. Notice the difference in hairs on the body and on the lower part of the leg of an insect. Study the hairs of plants, especially those of weeds. Compare the spines on burdock with the spines on a rose bush. Compare the scales of various fishes.

Blood

Blood contains two kinds of cells, red and white, and a liquid in which they float called the *plasma*. There are many billions of red cells in the human body; they live only about one hundred and twenty days. Every second about two and a half million blood cells die and the same number of new ones are formed to replace them.

A chemical known as *hemoglobin*, which is only in the red cells, gives the blood its characteristic color. The oxygen which we breathe in through our lungs is distributed by the hemoglobin to the tissues. Oxygen "burns" or oxidizes our tissues and food, thereby giving us energy.

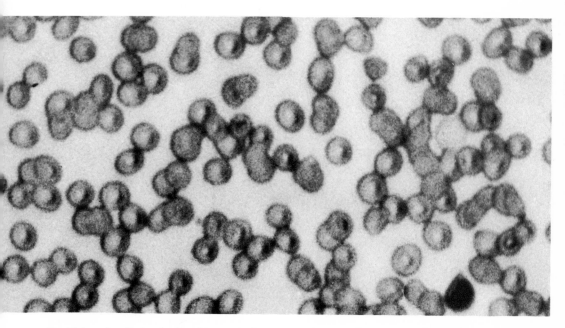

Red blood cells in the body are little disks, all exactly the same shape and size. Because of rapid coagulation of the blood on the slide, they may assume other shapes. When studying blood cells, work quickly before the blood dries.

The colorless white cells, called *leucocytes,* are the police force and cleaners of the blood stream. Any bacteria and other foreign particles entering the blood stream are attacked by leucocytes, which also remove broken-down tissues and poisons of the body. These cells, too, move fat particles wherever they are needed.

The blood fluid, or plasma, consists of about eighty per cent water. Dissolved in the plasma is the food material for the body which is carried to the tissues that need it. The plasma also helps to remove waste products. The substance *fibrin,* which causes coagulation, is produced in the plasma. When we cut ourselves, the fibrin forms a wall around the open wound which stops the blood from flowing out. This wall we call a blood clot.

Dust

One of the things that play an important part for good or evil in our daily life is dust. It comes from the activities of both nature and man. Windstorms over dusty soil and deserts carry tons of sand particles through the air for many miles. Ashes sift slowly down to the land from volcanoes that have hurled them upward and from meteors that have burned in the earth's atmosphere. The pollen of many plants is carried by the wind.

Much of the dust that floats constantly in the air is the result of human activities. It is these particles which are a menace to

Tiny dust particles revealed by the microscope in the grooves of a long-playing phonograph record. Such particles distort the sound reproduction. For good reproduction, the record must be clean.

our health, for many of them enter our bodies through the lungs and others are breeding places for bacteria.

The thousand of objects that we possess are always wearing down. The stones of houses, rubbed by the wind and cracked by heat and cold, lose fine particles. Particles of cloth and other substances wear off and float away on the wind. The greatest amount of dust in cities, however, is caused by the burning of fuels and refuse.

Dust is eliminated from the air by wind and rain which bear it away to the rivers and seas, and it finally settles on the ocean bottom.

The wonderful colors of the sunset are caused by the scattering of light by dust particles. Dust particles also play an important role in the formation of raindrops. When the water vapor of a cloud condenses, each drop is formed around a small particle of dust.

Gather dust from various places such as the park, the street on which you live, and a street near a large factory. In your home allow dust to collect on a slide. Under the microscope observe that the dust particles collected in one place are different from those found in another.

Cell structure of cotton.

Cloth

Since man has relatively little body hair to protect him against cold and heat, he has had to cover himself with materials that ward off extremes of weather. Innumerable centuries passed in which he wore only the hides of animals that he was able to kill. Gradually he discovered the means of making cloth from plant fibers, and then from the hair of animals and from the silk of the silkworm. Recently man learned how to create artificial fibers from chemicals. Cotton is a plant fiber and so is flax, from which we make linen. Wool and silk are the products of animals.

Millions of acres of cotton and flax plants are grown every year. Millions of sheep are allowed to roam the wide spaces of the United States, Australia, and Argentina for the privilege of cutting their hair, which is made into woolen cloth for us. The

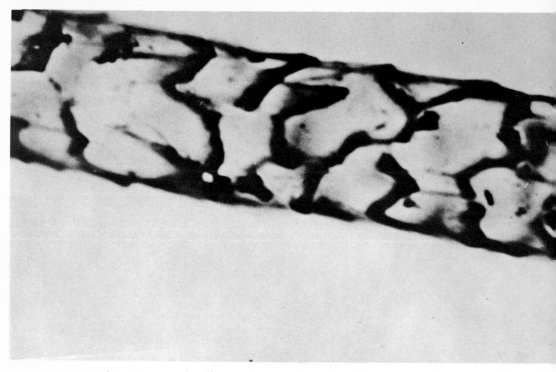

The outer wool cells overlap one another like the shingles of a roof.

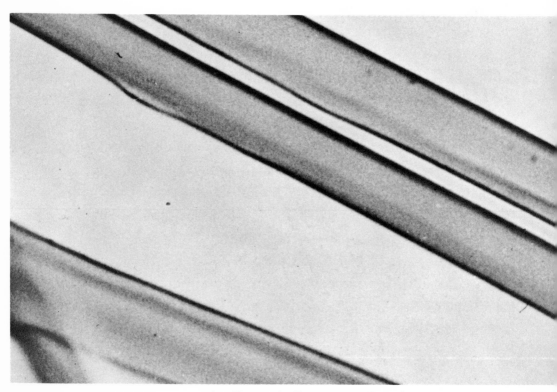

The fibers of silk are smooth and round.

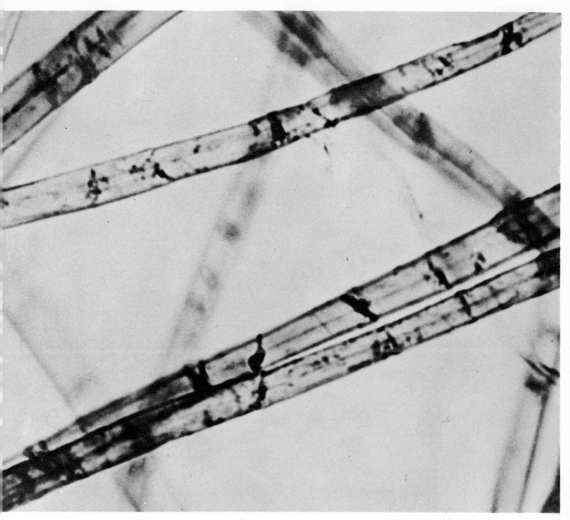

Flax cells.

caterpillar of one species of moth is given all the mulberry leaves it can eat, and when it forms its cocoon it spins the silk fibers which are used to make a fine gown for some lady who may live on the other side of the world.

Linen made from flax was woven by the ancient Egyptians and has been found in the tombs of pharaohs who died four thousand years ago.

The weaving of cloth has become a huge industry. Millions

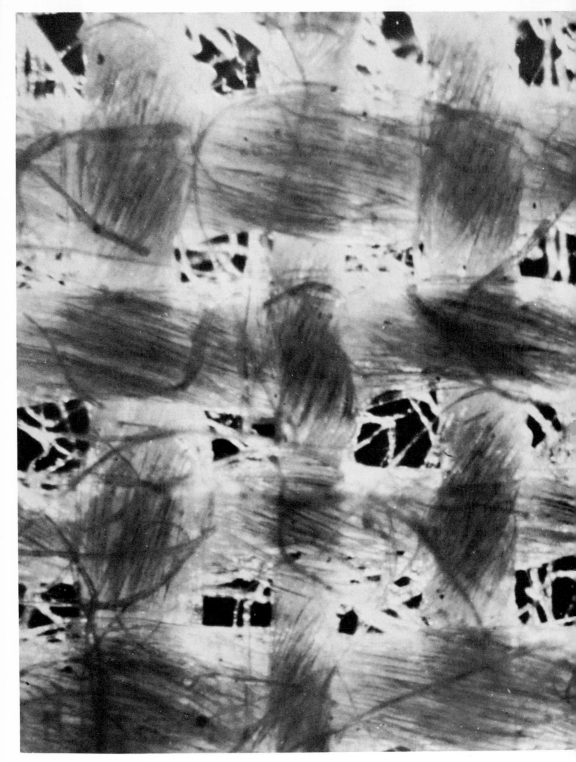

Weave of a linen handkerchief.

of men and women all over the world earn their daily bread by making cloth. Essentially the complicated machines of the factory differ very little in their weaving from the crude hand machines of primitive peoples. However, with the machine man is able to introduce a larger variety of designs and to produce hundreds of millions of yards of cloth annually.

Cloth is not only a shelter against weather, but also the most important means of adornment. It is natural that the desire for good clothes created a large demand for silk, since silk is one of the most beautiful cloths that we are able to make. But the demand is larger than the supply. Chemists solved this problem by producing an imitation silk called nylon. It is made synthetically from coal, air, and water and forced through minute holes under great pressure. This process forms fine threads which feel and look somewhat like silk. Chemists have also created other artificial fibers which are stronger than natural fibers. Some are wrinkle-resistant and retain creases even when wet.

Some cloth is a mixture of cotton, wool, linen, and man-made fibers. The microscope is useful for finding out what fibers have been mixed together in weaving the cloth. Each kind of fiber has a different structure, which is clearly visible under the microscope. For example, wool fibers are kinky and short; cotton fibers are straight and long.

Compare a silk fiber with a nylon fiber. Compare the weave in a handkerchief, a dress, a suit.

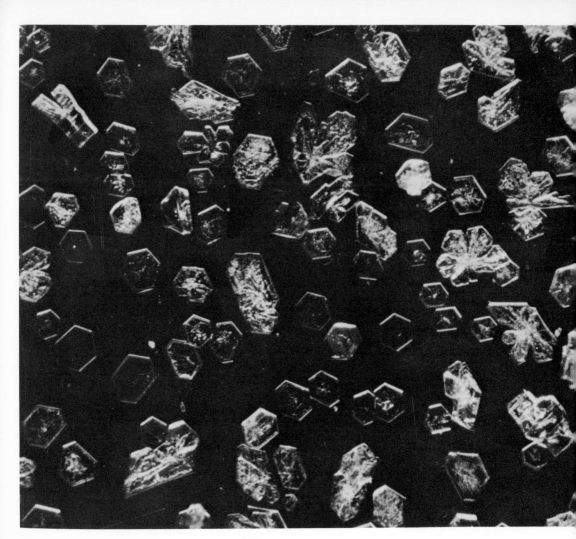

Crystals appearing in slowly evaporating solutions assume many beautiful patterns.

Crystals

All nature may be divided into two parts. One part includes all living things: human beings, animals, and plants. This is called the *organic* world. The other part includes all non-living things: minerals, metals, gases, and liquids. This is called the *inorganic*

164

world. Many inorganic substances, especially the minerals, are found in certain forms called *crystals*. Although organic substances also assume crystalline forms under suitable conditions, for the purpose of our microscope studies it is in the inorganic world that we look for crystal specimens. The science of crystallography is the study of crystals.

Searching for and collecting crystals is exciting and fascinating. Many are so small that we need a microscope to study them; others are so large that a single one makes a handful.

Crystals may be found wherever there is any rock structure. A quarry is a fertile place for the collector. Some beautiful crystals have been collected from building excavations. In the beds of small brooks or along the shores of waters where the underlying rock has been exposed by the pounding waves, fine specimens may be discovered. Thousands of crystals of many kinds and in many sizes may be found in caves.

The ardent crystal collector, however, will not limit himself to those crystals that have been laid bare by the work of nature or of other men. He will equip himself with tools—a hammer and a chisel—and wherever he sees a rock that may contain interesting crystals, he will investigate.

To understand how a crystal is formed one must know something about the basic structure of all substances. Every substance in the world is either simple or compound. A simple substance is called a chemical *element*. It cannot be divided into simpler chemical substances. Gold, iodine, and oxygen, for example, are elements. Anything which consists of two or more elements is called a *compound*. Water is a compound of the elements of oxygen and hydrogen; salt is a compound of the elements sodium and chlorine.

Salt crystals. Notice the broken crystals and the uneven crystallization.

The smallest possible quantity of any element is called an *atom*. When two or more elements combine to form a compound, it is the atoms which combine. The smallest quantity of water is one *molecule,* which is composed in the proportion of two atoms of hydrogen (H) to one atom of oxygen (O). This is written H_2O. Salt is composed of an equal number of atoms of sodium (Na for *natrium,* its Latin name) and of chlorine (Cl), written NaCl.

When an inorganic substance in a liquid or gaseous state solidifies, the atoms or molecules of that substance tend to arrange themselves in a definite shape called a crystal.

This process may be studied by making salt crystals. Heat a

small quantity of water and add common table salt to it until no more will dissolve. Get an absolutely clear solution. There should be no visible evidence of the salt, so that only your taste can detect its presence in the water. Although there is plenty of room in a glass of water for many particles of salt, eventually the water becomes saturated and no more salt will dissolve. When the water cools, a great many salt particles will come out of the solution in the form of cube-shaped crystals. All salt crystals have this shape.

Crystals increase in size as layer after layer of sodium and chlorine atoms deposit themselves on their sides. This process may be watched in a drop of the salt solution through the microscope. The first salt crystals are microscopic in size, but as more salt particles come out of the solution, the crystals grow larger and become visible.

The surfaces of each crystal are called its faces. Quartz, a hard glassy mineral, always forms a six-sided crystal. However, the sides may be so divided that they form several faces, and thus in the six-sided quartz crystal there are eighteen faces— three to each side. Water in the form of snowflakes always forms a six-sided crystal. Almost all inorganic substances form crystals which have shapes definitely their own. The characteristic shapes of the crystals of each mineral provide a method by which we can differentiate one mineral from another.

Not all crystals that we find in nature are perfect. If many crystals of the same substance or of various other substances are growing near each other, the pressure which each crystal exerts on the others forces them out of shape or stops their growth before they have reached complete crystal form. In a solution, in which the crystals are far apart from each other, this does not

The crystals of certain chemicals may have a flower-like form.

Left: A small, hollow stone called a geode, containing crystals of quartz and other minerals. Originally the minerals were in water solutions, which seeped into the geode and then evaporated, resulting in the formation of crystals.

Inside a geode are many crystals crowded together.

happen. When many crystals are crowded together in one mass without a single perfect crystal, this mass is called crystalline. Marble is a crystalline rock in which innumerable imperfect crystals of the mineral limestone are crowded together.

A mineral will not always form crystals. Under certain circumstances the atoms of the mineral are unable to arrange themselves in crystal form. Such a mineral structure is said to be amorphous, which means without form. Glass is a good example of an amorphous inorganic substance.

A rock is formed of minerals which are present in varying quantities. Granite is rock composed of the minerals quartz, feldspar, and mica. Not all granite looks alike. Its colors and textures may differ, as a result of different proportions of the three minerals which compose it.

Collecting crystals requires judgment and patience. In addition to the beautiful specimens gathered, the search will provide many joyful hours spent in the open, tramping over the good earth.

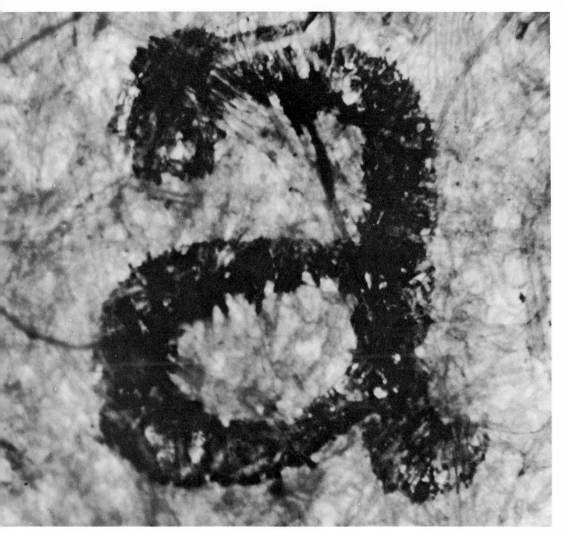

A view through the microscope of the letter "a" in a newspaper. Notice the fibers and structure of the pulp paper.

Paper

A hundred and twenty-five years ago paper was rare. Because it was expensive, children used pieces of slate instead of paper for practicing their writing. A thousand years ago the prepared skin of sheep, called parchment, was used for manuscripts. The

Chinese invented paper in the second century, but it did not become known in the rest of the world until the ninth century.

At first paper was made by hand, and such paper is still used for very fine books or for other special purposes. But today most paper is manufactured in huge quantities by machines. It is made mostly from wood, but very fine paper is made from linen rags. Newspapers, books, and magazines are made mainly from the wood of poplar and pine trees. The wood is cut into very small pieces and is chemically treated to remove impurities; then it is crushed, mixed with water, and boiled. This soft mass, known as wood pulp, moves over a belt of wire netting, which permits the water to drain off. The wood pulp remains as a rather spongy material which can then be rolled and pressed into thin sheets of paper.

Hand-made paper is of better quality than that made by machinery because the fibers are closer together, giving the paper a firmer texture.

Compare the fiber structures of different kinds of paper such as inexpensive yellow paper, a sheet of fine stationery, and those used in newspapers, magazines, and books.

How to Continue

Now that you have looked through this book while comfortably
seated in an armchair, why not make some discoveries for yourself? This book is a guide to the wonderful invisible world around
you. Select a subject that interests you. Read the chapter dealing
with that subject again. Collect your specimens and then inves-

173

tigate them with the microscope. When you have finished that subject, go to another one, and so on until you have gone through the entire book. Not until then will you know which subject is your favorite.

There is much for you to discover. Perhaps you will like your favorite subject so well that you will study more about it when you go to college, and then you may become a specialist in that field. Scientists are always needed. The world never has too many of them.

When you specialize in one subject, acquire as much knowledge about it as possible. There are many books on each one of the subjects. Always begin with a simple book and later read the more advanced ones. Go to your public library. The librarian will help you find the right book. If you live in a large city, there are biological and laboratory supply houses which may be of help to you. You may find their addresses in the classified telephone directory under the headings of biological, chemical, school, or laboratory supplies. Above all, ask questions about the subjects that interest you. Ask advice from the drugstore pharmacist, your teachers, your dentist, your doctor, the school librarian—from everyone.

Some may read this book during winter, when nature looks dreary and lifeless. The wind whistles through the bare trees, shaking the few remaining dead leaves on the branches. It may seem impossible to find any specimens for the microscope then, but if you investigate some of those dead leaves, you may find that cocoons have been fastened to them by caterpillars. Beneath the carpet of last summer's leaves, in the holes of trees, underneath stones, just below the surface of the soil and in the water, you will find many interesting organisms.

Select a few yards of ground. Go through it thoroughly. Investigate everything you see. You will be surprised at how many living creatures you can discover. The joy of making such discoveries is the reward of using your eyes.

Making notes and drawings of the objects you see under the microscope is a great deal of fun. Your notes should tell where and under what conditions you have found each specimen, and should record its size, shape, and color.

Remember, you are exploring new worlds through your microscope. Although hundreds of thousands of facts have been discovered, many more must be found. Young scientists, good luck!